D1093993

CLAYMORE AND KILT

Tales of Scottish Kings

and Castles

CLAYMORE AND KILT

TALES OF SCOTTISH KINGS AND CASTLES

BY SORCHE NIC LEODHAS

ILLUSTRATED BY LEO AND DIANE DILLON

HOLT, RINEHART AND WINSTON: NEW YORK CHICAGO SAN FRANCISCO

THIS BOOK FOR

Edna McFarland

Dear Friend and Kindest Critic

Contents

CLAYMORE AND KILT

Tales of Scottish Kings

and Castles

INTRODUCTION

hen a story from history is told there are always things that are not explained in the story about which readers would like to know more. For that reason, some of the historical background is given in this foreword to the tales in *Claymore and Kilt*.

In general, there is one thing common to all periods of Scottish history. From the very beginning English monarchs fought with all their might to make Scotland a part of England under an English king. And all through the centuries Scotland fought as fiercely to keep the country free and independent under a Scottish king. Rivers ran red with blood; castle, town, and village went up in flames: many great heroes of both countries lost their lives in battle. Then, after hundreds of years of fighting, Scotland and England were united peaceably when James VI of Scotland inherited the English throne after the death of the English queen, Elizabeth I.

There were many great kings in both countries, and many great warriors and great men all through the years of battles. No matter which side they fought on, it must always be remembered each and every one of them firmly believed his side was right.

This is the thread that holds all Scottish history together, like the warp of a loom, and each age presents the weft which shows the picture of its historical time. The eleven stories in this book present some of these pictures, and this introduction brings out some of the

211 A.D.   THE TALE OF THE SONS OF CATHMOR

No written records have come down to us from the ancient Caledonians themselves. All that we have to show about what these people were like and how they lived was written by Romans of the early times. Many of the Romans who wrote about the Caledonians never set foot in Britain, but wrote their books from stories told them by wayfarers and soldiers returning from that faraway island. It is not surprising that some of the information is not reliable.

Among the very early invaders of Britain was Julius Caesar who set foot on the shore of Britain between 55 and 50 B.C. In the sixth book of his Commentaries, Caesar explained this lack of books written by the Caledonian people. Caesar said that the Druids who were the wise men or wizards of the savage tribes ruled the tribes with great severity. Although in their trading and tribal financial accounts they used the Greek alphabet, the Druids would not permit their people to know and use it. In fact the Druids considered it unlawful to put into writing any of the history of their race. Caesar claimed that there were two reasons for this prohibition. One of these was that the Druids wished to keep the sources of all knowledge in their own hands so as to discipline better the common people. Only those persons the Druids chose to impart their knowledge were permitted to know it. This old history was in the form of druidic verses and there were so many that often a student was instructed for as long as twenty years before he could recite them all correctly. The second reason was that the Druids believed that if these records were allowed to be put into writing, the individual memories of the people would be impaired, because no man who knew he could refresh his mind by consulting a piece of writing would be willing to put forth the effort needed to commit it to memory.

Of course, most of this sacred knowledge vanished with the Druids, but the telling of stories, the oral tradition, persisted long after the Druids were gone and the Romans had left Britain forever. The old stories of Fingal are part of this old story-tellers' lore.

It has never been clear why Rome wanted to conquer Britain. Its people were no threat to Rome for they were not great seafarers. The island possessed no great natural wealth, although tin had been exported in small quantity from the mines of Cornwall for many years. Nevertheless over a period of nearly three hundred years Rome sent her generals with their armies to invade the land. The southern part, now known as England, was conquered easily enough and to some extent colonized. But when the Roman armies marched to the north, they had little success against the Caledonians. One Roman general after another came from Rome in those hundreds of years, and had his day in Britain, and then returned to Rome leaving the wild people of Caledonia very much as he found them—ferocious, savage, and untamed.

But in all these years, the Romans did a vast amount of building. In the southern half of the land, where the people were at peace, there were Roman villas, baths, and market places. All over the country were good hard roads and stone bridges, built by Roman soldiers. But in the north their building was of sterner stuff. Agricola, in 80 A.D., was the first Roman general who marched against Caledonia to subdue it. It was his intention to bring the savage tribes into a more civilized form of living, under Roman rule. But before long he found the job more than he had bargained for. The way the Caledonians fought must have been highly confusing to the well-trained Roman soldiers, who were accustomed to fighting in formation. A great screaming horde of savage Caledonians would come swooping down upon them, half-naked, painted horribly from waist to brow, and heavily armed. When the Roman soldiers stood to fight, the Caledonians divided their forces, racing rapidly along either side, doing what damage they could, until they reached the baggage trains. When they reached the baggage trains at the end, they cut them off from the main body of the Roman troops. Then, loaded with as much plunder as they could carry, they swiftly withdrew into the woods from which they had come, where the Romans could not follow or find them.

The word, Caledonia, the name the Romans gave the land, comes from one of their own Gaelic words, *coiltean*, which means thickets, or dense underbrush. It describes their country well, but a better name was the one that some of them called themselves—the Gaedil (sometimes spelled Goedhil). It means the stormy people, and certainly suits them well.

Agricola's building took the form of a line of forts from the Clyde River to the Firth of Forth and his work was completed in 85 A.D., about which time he was recalled to Rome. The purpose of the forts was to keep the Caledonians north of the line and to protect the more civilized dwellers to the south. The forts were not entirely successful, and the northern tribes worked such havoc on the southern peoples that in 120 A.D. the Emperor Hadrian, who had come to Britain for a while to see the new Roman colony, decided to abandon them and build a wall instead. Under his own direction, a wall was built that stretched across the country, dividing it in half. It ran from the river Tyne to the Firth of Solway, and it was admirably made and well garrisoned—but the Caledonians were able to get over it, just the same.

After the wall was finished the Emperor Hadrian returned to Rome, and nothing much was done about Caledonia for twenty years. Then in 140 A.D., when Antoninus had become Emperor of Rome, he was so disturbed by reports of the depredations of the northern tribes that he decided to have a second wall built. He did not go, himself, to Britain, as Emperor Hadrian did, but sent one of his ablest generals, Lollius Urbicus, instead.

Urbicus built his wall along the line of Agricola's forts, between the Clyde River and the Firth of Forth, some distance north of Hadrian's wall. But neither Hadrian's wall nor the wall of Antoninus kept the Caledonians out of the land between the two walls, nor even from the lands farther south.

These were the two walls built by the Romans which are spoken of in "The Tale of the Sons of Cathmor"

There is no historical evidence to prove that Fingal lived and ruled in these ancient times. Some historians consider him a purely legendary figure. Others say that there must have been, at some time in the early third century, a chief of that name who was so wise and so powerful that stories were made about his exploits, and handed down as part of the Druids' lore. It is true that there are scores of stories about Fingal and his son Osein and his warriors, and that they are not folk tales, but stories of battles and great deeds. Those men who believe that Fingal had an historical existence say that it is probable that he ruled in Argyll, and that he was the *Ard-righ*, or high-chief of the clans between the walls and on the western coast above them.

563 A.D.   THE TALE OF COLUMBA AND THE ANGEL

Columba was not the first missionary who came to Scotland. According to a writer named Eusebio, who wrote in 96 A.D., Saint Paul while on his missionary voyages traveled into Spain and from there sailed north until he came to the "islands of the far west" as Britain was called in those days. Then there was Saint Patrick who was, himself, of Scottish blood, the son of one of the western kings. Stolen away when a child by pirates, he was carried to Ireland, and there sold as a slave. When later, he became free and a famous missionary, he returned for a while to the land of his birth.

By the fourth century Rome had become a Christian city, and through the years when the Romans were settled in Briton, many of them had instructed their neighbors among the Britons in the new faith. The Roman Church was already the head of the spreading Christendom. Saint Ninian, born about 350 A.D. to wealthy Christian parents who were natives of Strathclyde, was sent to Rome to be educated. He returned to Strathclyde about 383 A.D. and became a devoted teacher of his own people. Saint Kentigern, also a native of Strathclyde in the Scottish Lowlands, carried on the work in

the sixth century, at about the same time that Saint
Columba was establishing his monastery on Iona in the
northern part of the land. Kentigern did not travel
widely, but he showed such gentleness and affection to
the people among whom he stayed that they gave him the
name of Mungo, which means "beloved one," and he is
known as Saint Mungo even now.

None of these men, great as they were, influenced
Scottish history so greatly as Columba did. The building
of the monastery on Iona, and the conversion of the wild
tribes of Pictland have given him lasting fame. For the
first time in their history these people could feel that
they were joined together as one people under the bond
of one religion.

From the beginning until its destruction by the pagan
vikings in their raids between the years of 793 A.D. and
850 A.D., the settlement at Iona remained simple and un-
pretentious. Yet its fame was so great that monks came,
not only from Ireland but from Europe to be trained as
missionaries within its walls. The early Church looked
to Iona as Islam does to Mecca. It was known as the Holy
Isle, and became the burial place of kings. Although
many of the records were destroyed in the raids, it is
known that forty Scottish kings, seven Norwegian, and
one French monarch were buried there. Fortunately for
history the monks of Iona, fearing that the monastery
would be attacked, sent some of their books and writings
away to safer places before the vandals struck. It is
from these that we now get the facts we know about the
monastery and the times in which the monks lived.

Columba's greatest achievement as a missionary was
his conversion of Brude, the king of the Picts. After the

king had wholeheartedly accepted the Christian faith, his people soon followed his example as a matter of course. It was the end of the rule of the Druids, for their control over the people was so completely lost that they could no longer find men to train in the old beliefs which, little by little, died.

It is sad to think that so much of the old historical lore of Caledonia perished with the Druids. The law they themselves made prohibiting written records was responsible for its loss. With no new scholars to learn the old verses, only the Druids who were left knew them. When their lives ended, most of the old stories of heroes, of courage, and of great deeds, as well as the mythology of the race, went with them to their graves.

Some of the stories survived—perhaps two or three score of them. It is possible that they were handed down by men who once studied under the Druids but later accepted Christianity. These, of course, are the stories still told, of Fingal and his son Osein. But if the lore of the Druids vanished, there are still records of Columba and his times. When you consider that there was no printing press and all the books had to be lettered by hand, it is amazing that so many of them were made. Some of them are amazingly beautiful in color and design.

Columba himself was a great writer, and besides his explanations of the Scriptures, he wrote some pleasant poetry. Some of the abbots who came to Iona after Columba's death wrote books about his life. One of these, Cumyn, who was abbot of Iona from 657–669 A.D., knew some of the monks who had known Columba, and from them he got many of the stories of Columba's life. It was

Adamnan, a later abbot, who tells "The Tale of Columba
and the Angel." It was told him by Cumyn and although
it may have been a dream, after all, both Cumyn and
Adamnan believed it was true.

THE TALE OF THE ROYAL EXILES *1067 A.D.*

Almost everybody believes that Duncan was slain in his
own castle at Inverness by MacBeth, ably assisted by
his wife Gruoch, that Duncan was a very old and helpless
man and that the crime was committed in the dark still-
ness of late night, while Duncan lay asleep. They further
believe that, according to a prophecy, Birnam Wood
came to Dunsinane, propelled by the hands of the soldiers
of Malcolm, Duncan's oldest son. This information has
been carried down from 1605, by means of the play
Macbeth, and unfortunately it is all historically wrong.

Shakespeare, in 1605, was badly in need of a new
play so he began to look about for material to use. He
came upon Holinshed's *Chronicles of England, Scotland
and Ireland*, a book of stories strongly legendary, but
supposedly historical. Shakespeare found in this book
Holinshed's extremely imaginative story of MacBeth.
Shakespeare had no intention of writing history. He
wanted to write a play that would satisfy the minds and
the emotions of those persons who would come to see it
performed. He took from the *Chronicles*, not only the
story of MacBeth, but parts of one or two other stories
in the book about other men, attributing their actions
to MacBeth. He changed a few things and added some
extra touches peculiarly his own, and when he was
finished he had one of the most perfect and most

wonderful plays of horror ever written—and hardly a word of it historically true.

The actual facts, after reading Shakespeare's play or seeing it performed, seem flat and colorless. There are no witches, no prophecies, no magic spells. What really happened according to history was something much more commonplace.

An invasion of Scotland was made by the Norwegian Earl of the Orkneys, Thorkil, with his brother Torfin aiding him. King Duncan with his army attempted to drive the invaders out of the country. MacBeth was one of Duncan's generals at the time. Both Duncan and MacBeth were grandsons of Malcolm II, but Duncan's claim had been considered the better when he came to the throne. The two men were cousins, and Duncan did confer estates upon MacBeth and such honors as were within his bestowal, but he could not be expected to give up the crown. MacBeth greatly desired to be king so, when Duncan's army was put to flight after a battle with the Norwegians at Burghead, MacBeth seized what must have seemed to him a favorable opportunity to revolt against Duncan. Some of Duncan's army joined him, and MacBeth marched with them against the king. Just beyond the village of Auldean at a place known as the smith's house (Bothgowan), Duncan was slain in a skirmish between his men and the men of MacBeth. That brought MacBeth's claim to the throne from second to first place, so he became king. Actually the throne should have gone to Duncan's oldest son, Malcolm, but possession was nine-tenths of the law. Malcolm was only ten years old, at the time, and could not have ruled the kingdom. MacBeth calmly disregarded the hereditary rights of

Duncan's son, and actually usurped the throne, basing his
claim to it upon his descent as grandson of Malcolm II.

Lady MacBeth was miles away at her castle in Inverness, so she gave her husband neither counsel nor assistance. The deed was done, not in the dark of night, but in broad daylight. Duncan was not an old gray-bearded man, as Shakespeare describes him. He had not long passed his thirtieth year.

It was the custom in ancient times (and not only in Scotland) for a king who had usurped his throne, as MacBeth did, to kill as many of the male relations of the dead king as he could. This was a logical move, for it made as sure as possible that there would be no one left alive to dispute the new king's right to the throne. That was the reason Duncan's friends rushed the two little princes out of the country. MacBeth's first thought would be to see that they were slain.

The English king, Edward, was the Saxon Edward the Confessor, and not one of the later kings named Edward who came along after William the Conqueror began to rule England. These later kings were numbered in the order of their rule, as Edward I, Edward II, and so on.

Strangely enough, MacBeth made a very good king, and was considered wise, just, and good-tempered. It was not until the last few years of his reign that his people complained of his rule. He had plenty of reason to be embittered. The Scottish earls, in many cases, had remained true to the memory of Duncan, and now, with their followers, they went over to the army of Malcolm, Duncan's son. When the Danish earls who were overlords of Northumbria, and particularly MacBeth's old enemy, the Danish Earl Siward, let it be known that they were joining the fight for Malcolm, MacBeth needed no witches or omens to tell him that his cause was hopeless. He put up the best fight that he could, under the circumstances, and died not at Dunsinane, but in a battle at Lumphanon in 1056.

As for Donald, Duncan's younger son whom Shakespeare calls Donalbaine, he was carried off to England with Malcolm after Duncan's death. Shakespeare makes them grown men, fleeing under their own power, but at that time Malcolm, as we have said, was about ten years old, and Donald four or five years younger. Malcolm was happy at the English court, but Donald hated the English so heartily that his guardians soon sent him to the Isles to live with his kinfolk there. Nothing more was heard of him until after Malcolm's death, when he tried to seize the sons of Malcolm but was thwarted. He did manage to become king for a year or two, but was driven out. A few years later, under Malcolm's second son, Edmund, Donald Bane was given half the country to rule as king. That, too, was soon taken from him, but he lived to be the true bane of Scotland for many a year.

1306 A.D.   THE TALE OF THE RIDDLE SENT TO BRUCE

There were ten kings in the direct line of descent between Malcolm Ceanmor and Alexander III. Although they were all great warriors and spent much of their lives in battle, most of them were wise and just, so that their people did not fare too badly under their rule in spite of the constant wars.

Of these kings the three who most influenced the times to come after them were David I, William the Lion, and Alexander III.

David I established the feudal system in Scotland and
so organized and strengthened the Church that it kept its
power until the times of James VI, nearly three hundred
years later. William the Lion was the unfortunate monarch who was taken prisoner by the English and made
to swear allegiance to the English king. So for a while,
Scotland was subject to England, but William the Lion
was able to purchase his freedom from the allegiance for
himself and his country when Richard the Lion-hearted
came to the English throne. Richard wanted to go on a
crusade to the Holy Land and was much more interested
in finding the money to do it than in ruling Scotland.
He permitted William the Lion to ransom himself for
100,000 marks—a tremendous sum for the Scottish people
to have to pay. However, times were not bad in Scotland
in those years, for the first payment of 10,000 marks was
paid without too much privation on the part of the people.
Only a token amount of the balance was paid, and that
unpaid debt helped to make trouble between England and
Scotland for a very long time.

Alexander III won back the Western Isles, the Hebrides,
from Norway in a great battle with Haco, the Norwegian
king. Indirectly, Alexander was the cause of the war for
Scottish independence which was won at Bannockburn by
Robert Bruce. If Alexander had not chosen to ride home
from a meeting on a foggy dark night, instead of waiting
for daylight as his companions begged him to do, he would
not have missed his way and fallen to his death over
the edge of a treacherous cliff. Alexander III left no
children to rule after him. His sons and his daughter
died before him, and when he died in 1286, the only heir
to the Scottish throne was his little grand-daughter
Margaret. The little princess was the only daughter of

Alexander's own daughter, who had married King Eric of Norway and had died a few years after the child was born. As Alexander's heir, little Margaret was Queen of Scotland and she would also be, one day, Queen of Norway as well, when her Norwegian father died.

Almost at once the Scottish nobles, objecting to a reign in which the difficulties of administering affairs for a child so young would almost immediately arise, began to consider the possibility of permitting another noble who could show that he was a descendant of the earlier Scottish kings to become King of Scotland in Margaret's place. There were some among them who attempted to force the matter by taking up arms, but the government soon put such rebellions down. There was no question that Margaret was rightly and by direct descent the one and only heir of her grandfather, and her claim to the throne could not be set aside.

King Eric of Norway also wanted his little daughter to become Queen of Scotland. The loss of the Hebrides by King Haco, who had been King of Norway before Eric came to the throne, was still a sore point with the Norwegian king. He had not expected that his little daughter would become Queen of Scotland. Alexander was not an old man when he met with his accident, and if he had lived he might have had other sons to inherit the throne. But now that Margaret had become her grandfather's heir, Eric saw that it would be possible to get the Western Islands back, for Margaret as the future Queen of Norway would bring them under Norwegian rule again. So greatly did Eric desire to accomplish this that he asked the most powerful person he knew to aid him to bring it about. That person was Edward I, King of England.

Nothing could have pleased the English king more than to
have a hand in Scotland's affairs. He had long wanted to
get control of that country, and to make Scotland and
England into one kingdom ruled, of course, by himself.
When the Norwegian king asked Edward I to help him
set his little daughter on the Scottish throne Edward saw
a very good way to achieve his goal peacefully, by marry-
ing his oldest son to the little princess. By this marriage
Edward's son would some day rule over the three countries, England, Scotland, and Norway. Consent to the
marriage was granted by the Scottish governors and a
betrothal by proxy was entered into between the little
Scottish queen and the English prince. Soon after this
Margaret was summoned to Scotland to take over the
throne, and to be married to the son of the English king.

The little future Queen of Scotland was just seven
years old when she set sail for her kingdom. The Scottish
people awaited her eagerly but she was destined never
to reach their shores. She had always been a frail child
and on the voyage the ship was so shaken and tossed by
tremendous storms that she became violently ill. Her
guardians ordered that the ship put in at the Orkneys
where the little princess was removed to a castle belonging
to a kinsman, but she never recovered, and in a few days
she died.

Now Scotland had no ruler at all, and so many claimants
to the throne arose that at one time there were as many
as eighteen. Each presented what he considered excellent
reasons why he should be king, and as there was no one
person or group of persons who had the authority to
choose one man from the claimants to wear the crown, and
each claimant had a large body of followers ready to take

his part, it began to seem that the matter would never be settled. Finally the nobles and the chief men of the Scottish Church held a conference and it was decided that an arbiter or judge should be chosen who would be appointed to decide which man had the best claim to the throne.

This was just the opportunity that Edward I had been waiting for. He had been sadly disappointed that his son was not to be married to the little princess who had died, but now he saw another way to get control of the Scottish government. He marched to Berwick with his army and sent word to the Scottish nobles that he was ready to be the arbiter they needed.

Perhaps the nobles and men of the Church were anxious to get the matter settled quickly. Certainly they were not thinking of what future troubles might arise if they chose the English king to be arbiter, nor how much power they were putting into Edward's hands. At any rate, they chose him as arbiter, and acceded to all his demands. His price was high enough, for he refused to act as judge except under certain extremely harsh conditions. He demanded that the claimants acknowledge him as superior lord of Scotland; that no claimant whose claim was rejected should afterward dispute his choice; that all the Scottish castles should be put in his hands; that the chosen claimant should swear allegiance to him when he had been crowned. There was not much Scotland could do by that time. Edward had his army with him, and Scotland was not prepared to go to war at the time. If his terms were rejected, the English king would certainly consider it a breach of faith. If they must choose between war with Edward I and peace under his domination, the latter seemed to be the better choice. So that was the manner in which Edward got Scotland into his own hands—for a while.

Edward quickly eliminated all of the claimants but two. One of these was Robert Bruce, the grandfather of the Robert Bruce in this story of the riddle of the coin and the spur. The other claimant was John Baliol, the Toom-Tabard of the tale. It is probable that John Baliol was chosen because Edward felt he would be easier to influence than any Bruce would be. It is certain that in the few years that Baliol reigned, Edward I so harassed him and humiliated him that after a feeble and useless re-bellion Baliol resigned the crown most willingly, and the way seemed to be clear at last for the English king to achieve his long ambition of making the two countries of England and Scotland into one country under his own rule.

These were the events that led up to the great war for Scottish independence. Robert Bruce, the disappointed claimant, must have been greatly satisfied when his grandson, another Robert Bruce, was crowned King of Scotland and put an end to the schemes of Edward I.

THE TALE OF THE WRATH OF GOD *1480 A.D.*

Of all the chiefs of the Western clans who were thorns in the flesh of the Scottish kings, probably there were none so troublesome as the Lords of the Isles. These chiefs ruled like petty kings over their islands and parts of the mainland Western Highlands, ignoring the kings and recognizing no authority but their own. And there is little doubt that the most trying one of the lot was John,

Lord of the Isles, the father of Angus of Islay, who liked to speak of himself as King of the Isles and the Western Scottish Highlands, although he had no right to the title at all. John and Angus between them managed to irritate two kings of Scotland (King James III and King James IV) to such a point that it ended in the loss of John's title as Lord of the Isles and all of his rights to the lands his family had held for generations.

John was, at the time of Angus' raids on Ross, at peace with his Majesty, King James III. He was quite right to fear that if Angus attacked the mainland estates, the king would believe that John had something to do with the raid. Although John always claimed that he had given up the lands of Ross and Kintyre with all their castles, as a voluntary gift to the king, in truth the gift had been forced from him as a punishment for an attempt to assist the English in a plot to seize Scotland for the English Crown. The English government, in 1461, had promised John, Lord of the Isles, that if he and his followers would rally the chiefs of the Isles and of the Highlands against King James III, their reward would be all the lands north of the Forth River, which was to be divided between John, Lord of the Isles, the Earl of Douglas, and the ruling chief of Islay, Donald Balloch. An attempt was made, too soon to suit the English, and although the Lord of the Isles captured Inverness with its castle, he was unable to hold it, and retreated again to the Isles. The Scottish government summoned him to appear to answer a charge of treason, but John refused to obey. For the time, the government paid no more attention to him. The king had other things to engage his attention and knew nothing about John's part in the English plot. If the authorities stopped to think of John's raid at all, they probably thought that John was just behaving in his usual manner, and were willing to overlook it until they had more serious offenses to bring against him.

For about fourteen years John managed to keep out of trouble, and it was not until 1475 that the Scottish government learned, through some documents which turned up at that late date, that John had made a treaty with the English government, and what the nature of that compact was. This was much too serious to overlook, and the Scottish Parliament sent for John to appear before the king to explain his actions. John flatly refused to obey the summons, but the king's anger was roused by John's high-handed behavior, so he made sure the arrogant chief would learn who was master of the land. King James sent a considerable fleet of ships, with an equally considerable force of soldiers, against the islands' chief.

John, Lord of the Isles, was not prepared to withstand such a great attack. He hurried to Edinborough as fast as he could to throw himself upon the mercy of the king. The king forgave him, but not until John had resigned his title as Earl of Ross and Kintyre, and presented the king with all the lands and castles which he had held on the western mainland. He hadn't much choice in the matter. He had to give up the lands, but he was allowed to consider it a gift. The king was lenient enough otherwise. He was allowed to keep his islands and his title as Lord of the Isles, and he was made a Baron and Peer of Parliament to soothe his pride.

All this had happened five years before Angus, the son of the Lord of the Isles, announced to his father his intention of getting Ross back. The last thing that the Lord of the Isles wanted was to rouse the anger of the king against him again. His war with Angus was not so much a sign of righteous indignation as an attempt to prove his good faith to the king. There is no evidence that the king's government believed him responsible for the raid on Ross by Angus.

Some years later, however, after King James III was dead and his son, James IV, had come to the throne, John of the Isles was at his old tricks again. His son Angus was dead, slain by his own harper, so John called his nephew, Alexander of Lochalsh, to help him in an endeavor to get possession of the earldom of Ross which he had given up to the father of James IV fifteen years before. The attempt failed and once again the Lord of the Isles was forced to throw himself upon the mercy of the king. James IV was not as lenient as his father had been. All the estates that John possessed were taken away from him, as well as his title of Lord of the Isles. John was left homeless, landless and penniless after his long years of grandeur. But after all, he must have been a likeable old rascal because James IV not only gave him a pension but permitted him to live the rest of his life in His Majesty's household at court. When he died, according to a request he made before his death, the king had him buried at Paisley in the tomb of his ancestor, King Robert II.

John was the last Lord of the Isles of his race. The lordship of the Isles has ever since belonged to the crown, and one of the titles of the heir to the throne is Lord of the Isles.

There is some difference of opinion among historians about the dates of the events told about in "The Tale of

A Popular History of the Highlands and Gaelic Scotland
gives the same dates that appear in the story about
Angus of Islay, and in this part of the foreword.

THE TALE OF A DEBT REPAID *1487 A.D.*

The great earls of Scotland, particularly in the Western
Highlands and the Islands, were like small kings each
ruling over his own domain and having infinite power
over the members of his clan. Under James II and
James III their power had grown immensely, because
James II, although a strong king and both wise and kind,
was too busy fighting the English to pay much attention
to the great chiefs of his own land. Unfortunately he
was killed while supervising his own cannon at the Battle
of Roxburgh. Weapons using gunpowder were still new
and the cannon were made of logs, hollowed and bolted
together with iron bands. One of these crude implements
of war exploded while the king was standing beside it
and he was killed at once. His son, James III, was a weak
king, and he had neither the love nor the respect of his
subjects as his father had. It could not be expected that he
would be able to do much about bringing order to the
Western clans. So they went on their merry way, fighting
their feuds and doing as they pleased.

Like kings and rulers of any country or any age, their
arguments with their neighbors led to war. The feuds
were fought for the purpose of settling who was right in
any dispute that arose. The side that won the battle considered that the question had been decided in its favor
by the victory, and that was the end of the matter until

another argument began over something else. Very often clans who a year or two before had been tearing each other to pieces would be found at a later date fighting on the same side. Most of the feuds were caused by quarreling about land boundaries or matters of the sort. Only when the offense was serious did ill feelings last through many years. The most famous example of a lasting grievance is the ill will between the Campbells and the MacDonalds which flamed high with the massacre at Glencoe and persists in a mild form, even today.

There was a decorum preserved in the feuds. The observance of set rules was demanded of those engaged in hostilities. Perhaps it was just as well, for the prevalence of feuds might have caused a state of chaos if there had not been some sort of order about waging war. The trouble was that the Highland clansmen had no settled occupations other than hunting or fighting. Their land was too poor and stony to cultivate, and the herding of sheep and cattle was not carried on to any great extent in these early days. The chiefs themselves were men of considerable wealth and even of education, who called their followers into a feud for reasons of policy or honor. To the fighting man the feud was a means of livelihood because of the plunder taken, which was divided among them all.

It seems strange that there was so little resentment of the looting, although it can't be supposed that the losing side liked it. When an invading clan came into their part of the country the non-combatants among the besieged—the women, the children, the crippled, the old—if they had time, buried the things they valued the most, or if hard-pressed dashed off with their treas-

ured belongings into a neighboring shire, out of the way
of the invaders. Perhaps the reason they put up with
it was that they thought, "Oh, well. Who knows? Maybe
next year husbands and sons will be bringing a load
of plunder home to make up for what was lost this
time."

At any rate, "The Tale of the Debt Repaid" presents a
picture of what a fifteenth-century feud was like.

THE TALE OF THE LADY OF THE ROCK *1527 A.D.*

By the beginning of the sixteenth century, things
were changing greatly in the world. Weapons used in
fighting wars used gunpowder, and the great long heavy
sword was being laid aside. Books, too, were printed
instead of being laboriously handwritten. Scotland was
not so quick to take up this new art as some other
countries, but her first printed book had been brought
out in 1508 A.D. In one thing, however, Scotland was
far ahead of many countries. Before James IV died
he had seen to it that a compulsory education act was
passed, making every baron and landowner (all the
gentry who could afford it, in fact) send his sons to
school, and afterward to the university. From this law
sprang the later village schools which assured the
common people an education, and gave Scotland the
lowest rate of illiteracy in the world long before other
countries had given the matter their attention. But if
the old medieval ways of living were changing, and
our Modern Age coming in, there was no change in the
lives of the Western clans as a whole. Feuds and fighting,
looting and plundering went on in the same old way.

36 The great chiefs were at the height of their power at the time that Lachlan MacLean of Duart marooned his wife on the lonely rock. Ten years later, MacLean would not have dared to attempt such a deed. The day was coming, although none of the chiefs would have believed it, if they had been told, when the power of the clans would be broken for good.

I have heard a number of variations of the story of the lady on the rock. One tale tells us that the Lady Elizabeth intended to leave her husband for a laird on the mainland, and MacLean put her on the rock to punish her. But history tells us that it was MacLean who wanted to get rid of his wife, because he wanted one with a larger dowry. Some of the versions have in them very odd supernatural elements. In one, the waves, hearing her prayers, bring to her a boat with a convenient pair of oars in it. The waves direct the boat to the rock against the pitiless tide, and she steps into it and rows herself to the mainland. From there she makes her way to her brother's castle. Her brother then sends for MacLean and makes him return the lady's dowry. One particularly witless but sentimental version has two angels come in answer to her prayers who snatch her up and carry her off to safety just as the rising tide reaches her chin. And an old ballad has it that MacLean put her on the rock in revenge, because she had men set off a charge of gunpowder which blew up the ship in which there was a Spanish lady with whom MacLean was in love. On the whole the story that sticks to historical fact sounds more convincing, and that is the one we have chosen to put in this book.

Although the Earl of Argyll was satisfied when MacLean had been driven from the Highlands, he was punished for his deed years later when one of the Campbells found him lying asleep in a poor room in a Wynd in Edinborough. The Earl of Argyll had ordered that no man of Argyll should sully his weapon with MacLean's blood. The Argyll man saw MacLean's dagger lying on a table by the bed, and remembering the Earl's orders, he picked it up and slew MacLean with his own weapon.

The Earl of Argyll in this story is not the same man who was Angus of Islay's father-in-law in "The Tale of the Wrath of God." That person was Colin, the first Earl of Argyll, and he was the grandfather of the Earl of Argyll who had a bonny young sister called Lady Elizabeth.

THE TALE OF THE GABERLUNZIE MAN *1531 A.D.*

When King James IV was killed in the terrible Battle of Flodden Field his little son was only a year and five months old. This was not unusual, for many a Scottish king met his death while still a very young man and left only an infant king to succeed him. The sad procession of unfortunate royal children moves through the pages of Scottish history. Often unloved, neglected, even mistreated, they were pushed aside to make way for their elders who were greedily ambitious to seize the rule of the land. In those days any man of noble birth who was able to take possession of the king's person was considered to have the right to rule in the child-king's name.

Before King James IV went to fight at Flodden, fearing that he might die in battle, he made a will appointing the queen as regent of his little son. In this way he hoped to avoid the battles among the nobles for the possession of the child. Unfortunately, the queen remarried soon after her husband's death, and in so doing was disqualified, and could not act as Regent for her son the king. At once a fierce fight began in which every noble fought, tooth and nail, to get the little king into his hands. For some time, like a bale of goods, little James V was passed from hand to hand, until when he was between eight and ten years old the head of the great Douglas family managed to seize him and carry him off to Falkland castle in Fife. The little king was kept a prisoner there, for the Douglases made sure that no one would take him away from them. He was closely guarded, always, by some member of the Douglas family, who knew that they would be able to govern the country only as long as they kept the king with them. No attention was paid to his education —when he was twelve he had not yet learned to read or write. Little provision was made for his physical welfare, he was given few pleasures, and was harshly treated by those who had him in their charge. As he grew older, no training was given him for the position he expected to attain, when he was old enough, as sovereign of the land. His guardians never spoke to him about what was being done in his name. Many historians have suggested that it is doubtful if James V would ever have lived long enough to become king of Scotland in fact as well as in name, if he had remained much longer with the Douglases. Their intention seems to

have been to keep him prisoner as long as he remained
alive and to go on ruling the country themselves.

Although untaught, James was anything but stupid.
Between his twelfth and his fifteenth year he managed
to pick up some of the knowledge that had been with-
held from him, probably from his attendants in the
castle. He always had a way with those who served
him which made them like him and wish him well. He
was clever enough to pretend to be weak in intellect and
childish in nature. He let his captors think that he was
quite satisfied to be where he was. But while they were
flattering themselves because they had him so completely under their control, the boy was quietly and
very secretly preparing to escape. In some way he made
two of the castle servants and a stable groom his con-
federates. With their help he managed to get word
to friends of his dead father who would help him when
he was able to get away. He waited until a time came
when the more vigilant of his watchers were away and
when the attention given him was less careful than
usual. Very early one morning, with the help of his
servants he made his way to the stables where the
groom had horses ready and waiting. The four of them
mounted at once and rode off at top speed. The heart
of the young king must have soared for joy. He was
not quite sixteen years old, he was having the first
taste of freedom he had ever had in his life, and friends
were waiting for him at his journey's end.

By the time James V was sixteen he had the rule of
the country firmly in his own hands. Scotland was in a
pitiable condition at the time. But the young king had
a tremendous courage, a firm determination to bring

order to the land, and ideas of no small value about how to accomplish what he meant to do. It was an enormous task for a boy of sixteen. But at sixteen, James V was not a boy. The hardships of his earlier life had aged him beyond his years so that in judgment and resolution he was the equal of any man among his peers twice his age or more.

The Douglases had been more interested in increasing the fortunes of themselves and their friends, connections or kin than in the welfare of the country. Scotland had not recovered from the great battle of Flodden Field, in which the king, James IV, and the finest flower of Scottish manhood had perished nearly fourteen years before. The land was ravaged by roving beggars, alone and in packs, thieving and terrorizing the country side. The chiefs of the Western Isles and of the Highlands considered themselves kings in their own right and paid no respect nor tribute to any government but their own. The Border was tormented by *reivers* (robbers) and *caterans* (cattle thieves) who kept town and country in a state of terror on both sides of the Border. With the government under the Douglases doing nothing to help them the people were hopeless under the load of troubles they bore.

It took James V three years to bring Scotland into a state of order. But that was a very short time, considering what was done. The beggars were subdued and forced to get licenses if they wanted to continue begging, and the penalties for theft and pilfering were unusually harsh and vigorously enforced. The Border *reivers* and *caterans* were tamed, and although there still were raids now and then, they were not carried

on upon such a large scale. And of these, with very good
wardens of the Marches on both sides of the Border, the
raiders who brought them off were usually caught and
punished sooner or later. As for the chief of the Isles
and the Highlands, they soon learned to fear the king's
displeasure. The old wild days were over and the power
of the Royal Government took the place of the power
of the little kings.

But it was the common people whose lot James V
wanted most to improve. All his life he preferred the
people to the nobles of the land. That was probably
because it was the common people, the servants of
the castle, who had given him the only kindnesses he
had known as a child.

In appearance he was not remarkable. He was not tall,
and although his face was not ill-favored, he was not
handsome as his father had been. He was stockily
built and very strong, and he had flaming red hair.
At first his people called him *Madahd-rhuad beag*—the
little red fox—but it was not long before they were
calling him "The People's King." He had the qualities
they most admired. He had courage, good judgment,
shrewdness and humor, and he knew exactly what he
wanted to do and how to get it done.

It was his firm belief that he could only know what
his people were thinking, what they had to complain
of, and what should be done for their good if he went
about among them, appearing to be one of themselves.
Much to the disgust of his nobles, the king was accustomed to slip away, over and over again, to travel
through the countryside in the garb of a countryman.
He might appear as a carter in a smock with a wagon

full of wares, or as a miller with flour dusting his
homespun frock. He might wear the dress of one of his
own pipers, or seem to be a shepherd with a small
flock of sheep. But the disguise he liked best and wore
most often was that long, blue, hooded robe that was
the mark of the gaberlunzie man.

The name which the Scottish people gave to their
licensed beggars comes from two Gaelic words: *gabaire*,
which means a garrulous fellow, and *lunndaire*, a lazy
lounger. Nothing could describe these men better for
they spent their lives roving idly about, gossiping with
anyone who would stop to listen, and much too lazy to
work at a trade. James V was a poet as well as a king,
and one very amusing song that he wrote is called
"The Gaberlunzie Man."

There were still wars to be fought and troubles to
meet so that James V was often too busy to do as much
for his people as he would have liked to do. But on
the whole, his people loved him and believed that he
was a very good king.

THE TALE OF THE LAIRD OF LOGIE
THE TALE OF THE RESCUE OF
    KINMONT WULLIE
THE TALE OF THE KING'S JEWEL

*1592–
1611 A.D.*

All these stories took place during the reign of King
James VI of Scotland, and at the time the Laird of
Logie made his escape the sands of time for Scotland
as an independent kingdom under a Scottish king were
running out very fast. In just a little more than ten
years, after all the battles between the Scottish people

and the English, the fighting would be over forever
between the two countries, and Scotland and England
would be united and at peace for the first time in
centuries.

James VI was the grandson of the People's King, and
the son of that beautiful and unfortunate queen, Mary
of Scotland, for whom nothing ever seemed to go right
in all her life. When she was seven years old, she was
married to the little Dauphin of France and at the
French court she remained until her husband's death
when she was eighteen. They sent her back to Scotland
then to rule her own country, since a new king had
come to the French throne, and there was no longer a
place for her in France. She could barely remember
Scotland, and she had no knowledge or understanding
of the people and their ways. They welcomed their
young queen at first, and were ready to like her, for she
had qualities they admired. She was beautiful, strong,
clever and extremely courageous, and so very young.

But to Mary of Scotland, after the sunny warm land
of France and the gaiety and the culture of the French
court, Scotland seemed cold and dark and dreary, and
its people rude and barbarous in their ways. In spite of
her beauty and courage, she had other traits that soon
lost her the goodwill of the people over whom she ruled.
She was headstrong and wilful and she refused to
listen to advice. She believed firmly that a monarch
ruled by Divine Right, and was not answerable to the
people for his actions, and in this belief she determined
to do anything she wanted to do. For six years she
ruled Scotland, while her government warned and ad-
monished, without changing her in the least. She made

two disastrous marriages, and her behavior so outraged her people that they would have no more of her. They demanded that she be deposed. Just six years after she came from France—she was not yet twenty-five years old—she was forced to sign a paper resigning the throne in favor of her little son. The Scottish governors, to make sure that the queen would not attempt to seize the throne again, sent her to England where she remained as the prisoner of the English Queen Elizabeth I, until her death.

So Mary's little son was crowned King of Scotland. He was just a little over a year old at the time. Once again Scotland had a king who was too young to rule for himself, and the battle among the nobles for the regency began again. The trouble was intensified by a body of men who called themselves the Queen's Lords, who were fighting to get control of the country and put Queen Mary back on the throne. They were able to get possession of the town and the castle of Edinborough and to hold them for some time. It was not until the fourth Regent for King James VI, the Earl of Morton, came to power that the Queen's Lords were finally vanquished.

Never was the conflict for the regency so bitter in any other reign. One faction and then another kept the country in a turmoil of civil wars. The first two regents, Moray and Lennox, were murdered by their enemies. The third died shortly after taking office, from his efforts in trying to preserve the peace of the kingdom. The fourth Regent, that Morton who defeated the Queen's Lords, fared better, but in the end he perished also. Morton was a cruel man and extremely greedy. He had

made many enemies who wanted to bring his rule to an
end. He had laid heavy taxes on the people, and most of
this revenue he took for himself, and he had devised a
number of other ways of building his fortune. Unfortunately he had no friends to help him when at last he was
called to account. When the young king was about fourteen, Morton was driven from the regency, and soon
after accused of being a party to the murder of the
father of King James VI which had taken place a few
months before the little king was born. He was tried,
condemned, and executed, although he insisted that he
was innocent, and had no part in the crime.

It must have been very difficult for the little king to
grow up in the midst of all this turmoil and confusion,
and to realize that most of it was centered upon himself.
He must have been a lonely child, for none of the men
who had him in their charge, his Regents and his tutors,
ever showed him the slightest affection.

He was not held prisoner as his grandfather, James
V, had been under the Douglases. His wants were provided for in a fashion fitting for a king. The man selected
to have charge of his education was George Buchanan,
who was the greatest scholar of his times. Buchanan
kept the boy so busy at his books for such long hours
that often the young king fell asleep over them, and was
punished severely for not attending to his lessons. But
James was clever, and the result of Buchanan's instruc-
tion was that he became the most learned king that ever
sat on a throne.

There was one thing that James was told by Buchanan,
by his ministers and controllers, over and over again.
They told him that a king was only the servant of his

people who would put up with him just as long as it pleased them to do so, but had the power to remove him if they wished. He was made to understand that they, his guardians, meant to keep the control of the government firmly in their own hands. James VI was, even as a child, extremely shrewd. He had it always in his mind that if he rebelled against those who were ruling for him he might lose his throne, as his mother had done, and possibly his life as well.

But if he could not rule for himself, he might amuse himself in any way he pleased, so he spent his days in hunting and hawking, and in the idle occupations of the court, and when he was called to show himself in Council, he was careful to say exactly what he was told to say. And no matter what faction happened to be in power at the time, he was clever enough to disarm them by pretending that what they were doing pleased him very well.

It was this very manner of appearing satisfied with everything which put the men who were called the Ruthven Raiders off their guard. They kidnapped the king when he was about fifteen years old and held him in Falkland Castle for a year and, as they had the king's person, they ruled Scotland for the time. The king smiled, and agreed to all they said, and signed the papers they gave him. He walked in the garden and amused himself by shooting arrows at a target, or reading a book. He seemed to be enjoying himself quietly and contentedly, so his captors forgot to watch him as carefully as they should have done. He was much cleverer than they expected a boy of sixteen to be. In some way, he managed to get in touch with friends who would help him, and one day when he was left unguarded for a while he

slipped away and succeeded in getting to his grand-uncle,
the Earl of March, who took care that the Ruthven
Raiders did not get him into their hands again.

So he remained free until he was eighteen, an age at
which he was considered to be old enough to rule without
a regent over him. It was no easy task, even for a grown
man, for Scotland was torn by religious and civil wars,
and by quarrels among the families of great nobles which
were as bloody as any of the old Highland feuds had
been. During the regencies, the Western clans and the
Border raiders had tried to regain the power they had
lost under James V. Although James VI did not have
the flaming courage his mother and his grandfather had
displayed, when he had to, he could summon forth the
strength and bravery that were needed in any situation
he had to face. He had to do so very often in order to
have his way against the will of his ministers, his Chan-
cellor, and the General Assembly of the Presbyterian
Church, all of whom tried to keep the young king under
their thumbs. Not until he was twenty-nine years old
was he able to feel that he was really the King of Scotland, with almost undisputed power. Even although he
was not as strong or brave as some of the kings before
him, he was much the shrewdest and wisest monarch
Scotland ever had, and so was able to accomplish more
than any of them had done. He managed to make his
nobles agree to live at peace with each other. He subdued
the fighting over religious issues and broke the power of
the Presbyterian Assembly over the State. And he established a force of mounted officers who very ably kept the
Borders in a state of calm they had never known before.
Of course, now and then an old rogue like Kinmont

Wullie would make a raid across the Border, but such events were few and far between.

Then one night in March, in 1603, a rider came galloping up to Holyrood Palace, where the King lay sound asleep. The gentleman who had raced up from London in such haste was Sir Robert Carey, and he had traveled day and night without stopping, for three whole days and nights, so that he might be the first person to bring grave news to the Scottish king. The English queen, Elizabeth I, was dead and, before dying, she had chosen James VI to follow her as King of England. So after all the centuries of fighting that had so torn the two countries, England and Scotland were at last peaceably united under one monarch, and soon would be one country, all the way from Dover to John o' Groats.

For Scotland, although a Scottish king sat on Britain's throne, it was an end to more than the battles. It was an end of Edinborough as the place of the Royal Court. The capital of the United Kingdom was the town of London, and the king and all his nobles moved to the English court. It was an end to the free trade with France, and Scottish merchants suffered greatly, for they had to pay duty on their wares, just as the English did. It was an end to Scotland as an independent kingdom. The Scottish people were ruled by the Parliament at London, and had to submit to laws made in what they considered a foreign land. And saddest of all, Scotland lost the privilege of having a king of its own. James VI of Scotland could not be claimed by Scotland any longer. He had become James I of England instead.

Long ago in Scotland in the days of the great Fingal there were two chiefs who dwelt between the walls built by the Romans. Cathmor was one of these chiefs and his domain lay westward along the banks of the river Clutha. Renowned among the kings of Scotland for his justice and wisdom, Cathmor ruled his people with kindness and they lived in peace, tilling the soil, tending their herds, and trading honestly with any strangers who came among them. By these means the country of Cathmor prospered and the people were happy in it.

Dunthelm, the second chief, was an evil man whose wickedness knew no bounds. Toward the east coast by the river Tuatha he built himself a fortress, and the town which straggled about it, in which his people dwelt, was poor and ill kept. They had neither crops nor herds, but lived partly by hunting and fishing and, for the rest, by raiding and robbing those who were weaker than themselves.

Day after day Dunthelm sat in his stronghold brooding blackly over the good fame and the wealth of Cathmor, until his heart was so filled with envy and hatred that he could bear it no longer. He leaped up then and calling his warriors about him he led them in a swift and sudden raid against the land of Cathmor. The people of Cathmor had no knowledge of the arts of war and fell an easy prey to the warlike men of Dunthelm. They made a brave attempt to defend their lord and themselves but were

*King Fingal
211 A.D.*

soon defeated, and in the battle the gentle Cathmor himself was slain.

To make his victory complete Dunthelm ordered that when the treasures had been removed, all the town and the land, and the people who had not been slain in the battle, should be put to the fire and the sword.

One of Dunthelm's men, more interested in plunder than in slaughter, left his companions and searched among the storehouses for anything of value that might have been overlooked, hoping to find some treasure to which he might lay claim. In a dark corner of one of the buildings he found the two young sons of the slain chief, clasped in each other's arms. Terrified by the horrors they had witnessed, they stood helpless, hiding their eyes and weeping bitterly.

Perhaps the robber was moved to pity because they were young and of amazing beauty. Perhaps he thought they might be useful to him to help him carry his load. Whatever his reason for sparing them may have been he did not trouble himself to say. He loaded them with the bundles of loot he had gathered and drove them along to Tuatha before him like a pair of young lambs. There he left them to grow up among the children of the town, and nobody bothered to ask who they were and nobody cared in the least.

Thus Calum and Colman, the sons of Cathmor, grew up and came to manhood among the enemies of their father, and the spirit of their father lived in them so that in this evil place they were not touched by the wickedness they saw each day. They grew tall and straight and strong and became so skillful in the hunt that no other duties were laid upon them. Dunthelm chose them to be his chief huntsmen, and they never were asked to join the warriors in their raids.

But the peaceful land of Clutha was not forgotten by the sons of Cathmor. Their hearts turned often to the happy days of their childhood and they longed to see their own country once more. They dared not ask Dunthelm for permission to go, knowing only too well that he would have their lives if he learned that they were Cathmor's sons.

One day while the hunters were pursuing a stag they went westward farther from Dunthelm's fortess than they had ever gone before. They found themselves on the bank of the Clutha river and the brothers knew that they were not far from their former home.

The young huntsmen found a pretext to send their companions back to Tuatha while they themselves went on along the river until they came to the place where Cathmor's town once lay. When they saw the ruins of the once proud hall of their father and the lonely and desolate fields that had once been fruitful, now given over to thistle and bracken and peopled only by the fox and the owl, Calum and Colman wept for grief. Calling upon the spirit of their murdered father to witness their words they swore that while they had breath and blood in their bodies, the wrong done to Cathmor and his people by Dunthelm would not be forgotten nor left unavenged.

Among the huntsmen there was one Carach, a sly and sullen man, who resented the honor Dunthelm had given the brothers. He felt that the place of chief huntsman was his by right, and for a long time he had spied upon Calum and Colman, hoping to catch them in some act which would bring Dunthelm's wrath against them and win approval for himself.

When the other hunters turned back toward Tuatha as they were bidden, Carach did not go with them but secretly followed after Calum and Colman instead. Safely hidden in the upspringing brush he listened to everything the brothers said, then satisfied that he had in his possession the weapon which would cause their downfall he slipped off noiselessly, and with great speed made his way to tell Dunthelm what he had heard.

When Carach told Dunthelm that his two chief huntsmen were the sons of Cathmor and that they were planing to avenge their father's death, Dunthelm's fury was like that of a madman. He swelled with rage and his face grew purple and he roared like a wounded wild boar. He dashed to the floor the flagon from which he had been drinking, and knocking everyone and everything within reach out of his way, he strode out of his hall. As he stood for a moment at the top of the steps that led to the courtyard below, Carach imprudently attempted to gain the furious chief's attention. Perhaps he hoped to win a word of approval for the service he had done. But he had chosen the wrong moment. Dunthelm, with a sweep of his arm, brushed Carach out of his way with such force that the spy tumbled head over heels down the steps to the hard-packed earth of the yard below, and there he lay. All the reward that Carach won for bringing his news to Dunthelm was a broken neck!

At that moment, Calum and Colman returned. Without delay the brothers were seized at Dunthelm's orders, and securely bound. Calum was placed in a cave by the shore to be drowned by the rising tide, and Colman was

lowered into a pit near the wall of the fortress and left
there to die of hunger and thirst.

Dunthelm's only child, a daughter named Thalmar, had grown up neglected and uncared for, despised by her father because she was a girl. Her heart had long since turned from her father because of his evil ways. Then, too, she blamed Dunthelm for the death of her mother who had been treated with such cruelty by the chief, because she had borne him no sons, that at last the poor lady sickened and died.

Calum and Colman had won Thalmar's liking by their kindness and courtesy. Both qualities were rare among the other men of Dunthelm's stronghold. Now she determined to help them as much as she could to escape the fate to which her father had doomed them.

In the late hours of the night when all in the castle were sleeping and even the guards dozed at their posts, she crept soundlessly to the armorer's room and searched there until she found armor that she was able to wear. She clad herself in the battle dress of a young knight who was nearest in size to herself, and twisting her long hair firmly on top of her head, drew a helmet over it to hide it out of sight. Sword and spear and shield were too heavy for her to carry so she left them behind and took for weapon only a dirk which she stuck through her belt.

She slipped out of the fortress by a small postern door where one guard slept noisily and did not waken as she passed by. She picked her way in the darkness down the path from the gate through brush and bracken, until she reached the shore. Then with the fortress far enough behind her that she had no fear of being heard, she went quickly along the sands until she came to the cave where Calum lay helpless, waiting for death.

Thalmar knelt beside him and cut the ropes which bound him, then helped him to his feet and out of the cave which had so nearly been his tomb.

Calum recognized the armor which Thalmar wore, but not knowing it was not worn by its owner, called her by the young knight's name and thanked her for coming to his aid.

"If it were not for you, O Dionach," he said gratefully, "this night most certainly would have been my last."

And Thalmar, her identity safely hidden by helmet and armor, accepted the name of Dionach which Calum mistakenly bestowed upon her and let him believe her to be the young warrior whose armor she wore.

Calum's first thought was for his brother and he would have rushed to his aid at once had the young knight not held him back. She reminded him that four warriors kept watch in the courtyard through the hours of the night, two waking while the others slept. The pit where Colman lay could be reached only by passing the guards, and how could they, being only two and unarmed, hope to overcome four armed men, since the two who slept would certainly be awakened at their approach? What help would it be to Colman if his rescuers died in their attempt to save him?

Calum weighed in his mind the words of the young knight, and found them heavy with wisdom. In despair and sorrow, he cast himself down upon the sands to lament his helplessness. Then the young knight said to

Calum, "Come! Waste not your time in grieving. Let
us go to King Fingal and entreat him to help us free
your brother. I know the way to Morven, the kingdom
of Fingal. I will go with you and be your guide."

So they set out together, halting their journey only
for such sleep as they needed and for such food as they
could find on their way.

When they came to Morven they found King Fingal in
his castle at Selma, sitting in his chair of state among
his chiefs. Fingal called them to him, bidding them welcome if they came in peace, and asked them who they
were, and whence and for what purpose they had come.

Calum answered that he was a son of Cathmor of the
Clutha and his companion was his friend Dionach, to
whom he owed his life. They had come from the Tuatha
to ask Fingal's help against Dunthelm, the chief.

"Son of Cathmor?" said Fingal. "They told me that
Cathmor and all his family and his people perished
years ago in a battle with the warriors of the Tuatha."

"Cathmor and his people were slain," said Calum,
"but not in battle. They were attacked without warning
and unarmed when Dunthelm and his men came down
upon them suddenly. But Cathmor's sons still live. I am
Calum, the younger, and my brother Colman is being
held prisoner by Dunthelm. It is for my brother's sake
I ask your aid."

"Calum, Son of Cathmor," said Fingal. "Lay your
grievance against Dunthelm, the chief of the Tuatha,
before us that we may judge if thy complaint be just."

Thus at Fingal's bidding Calum and Dionach made
their accusations against Dunthelm and to every offense

laid at his door by Calum, Dionach added another, until the chiefs of Morven marvelled that one man alone could bear such a load of iniquity.

They spoke, but Fingal heard them without breaking his own silence. He made no comment and he asked no question, as the tale unfolded. Only by narrowed eyes and the set, grim lines of his face did he show his increasing wrath. But the silent anger of Fingal was more terrible to behold than would have been the unleashed fury of a lesser man.

When the accusers of Dunthelm were silent at last, Fingal rose from his chair. Standing to give judgment he spoke of the ancient friendship between the fathers of Fingal and Cathmor. The arms of each had hung through generations upon the walls of the other, and their children had been exchanged in fosterage. When word of the death of Cathmor had been brought to Fingal he had mourned for him as he would have mourned for a brother. Not until this day had he known that Cathmor was slain, not in battle, but by Dunthelm's treachery. From time to time Fingal had heard of the misdeeds of the chief of the Tuatha but he had not learned the full extent of his wrongdoing before. It had been in his mind of late, however, that the time was approaching when Dunthelm must be called to account for his actions. Now, Fingal said sternly, the time had come. It should be attended to.

Then, to avenge the death of Cathmor and for the sake of the sons of Cathmor, Fingal called up his mightiest warriors. He arrayed them in shining armor and armed them with shields and spears in their hands, and broad swords and dirks at their sides. He divided them among the chiefs of Morven, one hundred warriors to each chief, and sent them against Dunthelm.

So they marched, a terrible army, across the land, turning neither to left or right, nor staying on their way until they came to the shore of the Tuatha and saw on the other side the stronghold of Dunthelm with the evening mists from the river just beginning to settle down upon it.

When he heard the noise of Fingal's army as it approached the opposite shore, Dunthelm brought his men out and drew them up on the plain before the fortress to face the warriors on the other side of the river.

Then the bards, as was their custom, advanced from the line of the army of Fingal and went down to the river. Standing at the edge of its waters they shouted out the challenge to the chief of the Tuatha across its flowing tide.

"Hear and heed, O Dunthelm!" cried the bards.
"Hear and heed, O Dunthelm!"
"Hear and heed, O Dunthelm!"
"Deliver Colman, the son of Cathmor, to Fingal of
    Morven, or prepare to perish at the hands of
    the warriors of Fingal the Mighty!"

Three times the bards repeated the challenge, and their voices rang loudly across Tuatha's stream. Then they turned and rejoined the army to await the answer of Dunthelm.

Dunthelm's answer came swiftly. Driven mad by rage, he ordered two of his men to raise Colman from the pit and bring him to the bank of the river. There Dunthelm slew Colman with his own spear before the eyes of his brother Calum and all the army of Fingal on the opposite shore.

Calum, seeing Colman fall and his life blood pouring out to stain the sands upon which he lay, rushed forward. Plunging into the river he crossed it swiftly and hurled himself upon Dunthelm. With a mighty shout the warriors of Fingal pressed close behind him, and thus the battle began.

Swords flashed, spears leaped to their marks, shields clanged under the blows that rained upon them. Dunthelm attempting to defend himself from the furious attack of Calum, found that he was no match for the younger man, whose strength had grown sevenfold through his determination to avenge, once and for all, the deaths of his father and his brother, or to perish himself in the attempt.

The cowardly Dunthelm, unused to standing against an opponent who was not weaker than himself, sought safety in flight but Calum pursued him and despatched him with one last thrust of his sword.

Dunthelm's men knew they were outnumbered and when they saw their chief fall they gave way and attempted to retreat to the fortress. But they soon found they were cut off from that refuge for the men of Fingal had contrived to surround them on all sides.

When the battle was over and Fingal's warriors entered Dunthelm's stronghold to make certain that no stragglers were hidden there, it lay silent and empty. The chief of Tuatha with all his men lay dead on the river's shore.

There was not a living soul left in the fortress or in the town, for the women had taken the children and fled, when the battle began, to hide in the woods and the caves. No one sought to find them or harm them. Fingal's men, unlike Dunthelm and his warriors, did not make war on the weak.

By the time the battle ended, night had fallen. The men of Fingal made for themselves a mighty torch. They laid fire to the fortress and by the light of the flames they tended their wounded and gathered their dead, waiting until the daybreak to return to Morven again.

At dawn, they took the body of Colman and those of their companions who had not survived the battle and crossed the Tuatha to start their journey home.

There they found the young knight called Dionach who had come to Fingal with Calum. Now they discovered that he alone of all the warriors had not crossed the Tuatha, but had watched the battle from the safer side. They found Dionach wandering up and down, dragging behind him a spear which had been discarded for the sword by one of Fingal's men when the battle began.

The warriors were wroth against Dionach. They called him coward and traitor, and asked him if he was a cat, that he feared to wet his feet in the river. But when they moved to lay hands against him, to hang him for his cowardice, Calum set himself between them and the young warrior. Dionach had saved him from drowning, he told them, when he lay bound in the cave. They should not harm Dionach, he said angrily, unless they slew Calum first.

When the men of Fingal saw that Calum dared to

stand alone against them they admired him for his great courage, so they spared Dionach and took him with them to Morven where they left it to Fingal to decide what his fate should be.

A time was set for mourning the death of Colman and the warriors who had fallen in the battle of the Tuatha. When it had passed, Dionach was brought before Fingal to hear the king's decision.

"Never before has a coward been found in the army of Morven," said Fingal with scorn. "If you were afraid to fight, why did you not remain here with the women? Could you not find courage to strike even one blow in the battle?"

Dionach made no reply, but stood silent with his head lowered as if in shame. So the king, when he found the young warrior offered no word in his own defense, pronounced his judgment against him.

"Never again shall you wear the armor of a warrior," said Fingal. "From this day you shall go clad in the attire of a woman. It will be more fitting for you than the armor you wear." And with his own hands Fingal tore the helmet from Dionach's head.

Down tumbled the masses of long dark hair the helmet had so cunningly concealed, and the face of Thalmar looked up at Fingal. In amazement, the king let the helmet drop from his fingers, and stood speechless, staring at the girl.

"O mighty Fingal!" Thalmar said gravely. "A woman's attire will surely be more fitting for me, since, as you see, I am a woman, and was never intended by nature to be otherwise. I only borrowed the armor for a while because it seemed wise to do so." Then she added with

some spirit, "But the king shall not call me a coward. I was not afraid to fight. The spear was too heavy for my strength. I could not lift it to give even one blow."

Fingal found his voice and the hall resounded with his laughter.

"She could not lift the spear!" he shouted. "And what better reason for not striking a blow?"

He turned to Calum, whose surprise was no less than that of Fingal. "Who is this warrior-maiden you brought to us?" he asked.

"She is Thalmar, the daughter of Dunthelm," answered Calum. "But I did not know—I thought she was Dionach, one of the warriors of the Tuatha. The armor is that of Dionach."

"We should have had the armorer make a spear that was not too heavy," said Fingal. He took Thalmar's hand in his own.

"Whether she be Dionach or Thalmar," the king told Calum, "the maiden has been a good friend to you. To begin with she saved your life, and then she led you to me. And she followed you into battle. Aye, and had she been able to wield the spear, no doubt would have struck a good blow or two in your behalf." Then he reached for Calum's hand and laid Thalmar's in it. "Here!" said Fingal. "You had better have her for a wife!"

Well, old feuds die out and new friendships grow in their stead. Cathmor and Colman were avenged and Dunthelm had received the punishment he deserved. Thalmar could not mourn for the father who had despised and hated her, and whom she had never learned to love. The countries bordering on the lands of the Tuatha were safe forever from Dunthelm's raids.

Thus Thalmar and Calum plighted their troth at the
court of Fingal and in due time became man and wife.
The estates of Cathmor were restored to his son, Calum.
Dunthelm's lands were given to Thalmar for her dowry.
And in this way the lands of the Clutha and the lands of
the Tuatha were united and, ruled wisely, were peaceful
and prosperous, and all was well in the end.

King Conall
563 A.D.

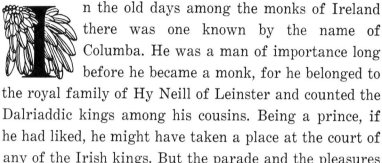

I n the old days among the monks of Ireland there was one known by the name of Columba. He was a man of importance long before he became a monk, for he belonged to the royal family of Hy Neill of Leinster and counted the Dalriaddic kings among his cousins. Being a prince, if he had liked, he might have taken a place at the court of any of the Irish kings. But the parade and the pleasures of kingly courts held no charm for Columba. He chose instead to become a monk.

A monk he was, then, and one of the best of them all, going up and down the whole of Ireland, preaching the word of God. Great was the fame he won in his own country for his learning and wisdom. Many were the churches he built and the monasteries he founded and he was known from one end of Ireland to the other, not only for the fire of his preaching, but for the warmth of his heart.

But after a while Columba began to feel that Ireland wasn't needing him any longer. There were plenty of monks in the monasteries, all good men and well able to do any work that had to be done.

" 'Tis high time I put my days in Ireland behind me," said Columba, speaking to himself. "I'll have to be looking elsewhere to find a new place to be sowing my Holy Seed."

There were merchants and travelers in those days, going back and forth between Ireland and Scotland,

and some of them brought strange tales to Columba about the wild savage tribes called Picts who dwelt in the land across the sea.

"You'll not be seeing the like of these lost souls in a yearlong journey in Ireland," they told him. "The poor benighted souls have never heard of God! They have a class of priests called Druids that rule the people by fear. These wicked and cruel men tell the people the world is full of demons that dwell in the trees and streams, and that nobody but the Druids are able to control these evil spirits. The people are so afraid the Druids will let the demons loose to destroy them that they will do anything the Druids tell them to do."

" 'Tis beyond believing!" exclaimed Columba.

"Aye. But 'tis true," the travelers said.

After the travelers went on with their travels, Columba could not get the tales they had told him out of his mind. He used to stand on the Irish shore and look across the sea toward Scotland with a great longing in his heart to go there and free the wild Picts from the Druids' power.

Long before the time of Columba, Irish Scots had made a settlement on the west coast of Scotland, which they called Dalriadda after the Irish kingdom of that name. The colony had prospered and grown until it had become a kingdom with a king of its own. Now the king of the Scottish Dalriadda was Columba's own cousin, Conall. The cousins had never met, but that made little difference. A blood-tie was the best introduction a man could have if he was going to ask for something. Columba had it in his mind to ask a favor of his cousin Conall.

Columba had heard of an island known as Iona which lay off the west coast of Scottish Dalriadda. Iona belonged to Conall's kingdom, but few of his people lived there because it was a remote and lonely place. The island was not of much use to Conall, Columba thought. So why shouldn't he go and ask his cousin to give Iona to him? He'd build a monastery there, and train monks to be missionaries, and send them out from Iona to go among the Picts.

Columba wasn't the sort of man to be letting grass grow under his feet. Once he got a notion in his head he acted upon it without delay. He went around to all the monasteries he'd founded and picked out twelve good strong monks. There were twelve in memory of the first twelve Apostles, they must be good because their goodness would be a weapon against the wicked Druids, and they had to be strong, because the life ahead of them would take all the strength they possessed. He asked only for twelve, but he could have had a hundred—or more. There were many who wanted to go. But Columba chose the dozen he wanted, and consoled the rest by telling them they could come to Iona later, if everything went well.

So one bright day, under a sky that was blue and cloudless, with the sun shining down and tipping the little dancing waves with gold, Columba and his twelve companions set sail across the sea to Scottish Dalriadda. And, looking about him at the beauty of the day, Columba took it as an omen that God would prosper his work.

When Columba presented himself at the court, King Conall welcomed him warmly. Dalriadda had need of Columba and his monks, said Conall. He hoped their visit to his country was going to be long. Conall was so pleased to learn that the monks were not intending to return to Ireland that, when Columba asked him to give him Iona, Conall granted Columba's request without question, and had the deeds prepared for Columba at once.

The monastery Columba and his monks built on Iona was nothing great to behold. They erected a church, which was small and low and humble, and around it they built a few rough huts for the monks to dwell in. Around church and huts a wall of earth and stone served as protection against the winter waves and wind. But, poor though it was, it served its purpose and Columba asked for no more.

Monks began to go out to Pictland from Iona, and as the fame of the monastery grew, more monks came to join them. Within a few years the monastery was a busy thriving place with men flocking to Iona from Ireland and Britain and even from farther countries to be trained as missionaries, and with monks going out or coming back every day. The good omen of Columba's sailing had come true: the work had prospered and Columba had his heart's desire. The poor wild creatures of the traveler's tales were being freed from the Druids, and were accepting the kindlier beliefs of Christianity.

Columba was not so wrapped in his missions to Pictland that he forgot Dalriadda. At Conall's request he sent monks all through his cousin's country to build churches and preach to the people.

A great friendship had grown between Conall and Columba. They relied upon each other for advice and comfort, each greatly trusting the wisdom of the other. Columba, as Abbot of Iona, was often at court and, as advisor to the king, had great influence there.

In the thirteenth year of his reign, when Columba had been about ten years at Iona, King Conall died. Columba was deeply saddened by his cousin's death, and to the burden of his grief was now added a heavy responsibility.

Now that Dalriadda had an abbot of its own, it fell to the lot of Columba to choose the successor to the king. At this time it happened that there were two men who claimed a right to the crown of Dalriadda. It was up to Columba to decide which one of the two would be the better king for the country, and most fit to reign in Conall's place.

The two nobles in line for the crown were Eoghan and Aidan, both of whom were well known to Columba, who had met them often at court. As far as their rights to the kingdom went, the claim of the one was as good as that of the other. The only way that Columba could find to decide which one would be best as king was to judge them by their characters.

"There's little to choose between them," Columba said to himself. "They're both good fellows, and the people like them both. Choosing between them is going to be no easy task."

So he put his whole mind on the matter, keeping an eye on the two, and weighing the merits and faults of each against those of the other. But as the time allowed for deciding passed, he came no nearer to making up his mind. Although he might have admitted, if asked, that he was a bit inclined to favor Eoghan, still he was far from ready to make a choice.

He came to the last week left to him, with the time

slipping by. He had seven days left to make his choice—
then six days—five days—four days. And on the fourth
day of the last week before he must name the new king,
he overheard Eoghan and Aidan having an argument,
and going at it hammer-and-tongs.

'Twas all about some dispute that had started between
the two Dalriaddas, the one in Ireland and the one in
Scotland. Aidan was all for getting an army together
and going over the sea to settle the matter by force of
arms. But Eoghan could see no sense at all in fighting
for what could be settled more safely and comfortably,
by letting the ambassadors of the two countries talk it
over. Besides, it would come out much cheaper in the end.

Well, they kept the argument up for some time and
neither convinced the other, but between them, they
helped Columba to make up his mind at last.

" 'T would never do to have Aidan ruling the country,"
Columba said to himself. "He'd pick a new quarrel with
the Irish kings every month of the year. He's too hot-
headed and impulsive to ever be safe. Nay, Eoghan's
the man for my money. He's cautious and maybe a bit
inclined to be lazy, but with him on the throne the
country would be at peace."

That same night, when Columba had gone to his hut
and sat there at his table engaged in setting down the
record of the day, an angel appeared before him bearing
in his hands a book with cover and pages of shining
crystal. The angel opened the book to a page which he
held before Columba that he might read. On the crystal
page was inscribed the name *Aidan* as king after that of
Conall who was lately dead.

"Nay!" exclaimed Columba, shaking his head. "Not

Aidan. I have chosen Eoghan to be king."

As he spoke the angel disappeared. Columba, finding himself alone sat, dazed and wondering. But in a minute he told himself "I must have fallen asleep here at my table. I have been dreaming." So he put up his pen and closed his books and laid himself down upon his bed.

When he woke in the morning, Columba remembered the angel. "I have not had so strange a dream before," he said. "But I am not one of those foolish people who let dreams direct their acts. I shall send for Eoghan in two days' time and proclaim him king."

But that night the angel appeared again, and Columba, looking up from his books, saw him standing with the crystal book in his hands as before. The angel opened the book and with his finger pointed to each letter of Aidan's name.

"Nay! Nay!" protested Columba, annoyed at the angel's persistence. "I will not have Aidan. Eoghan must be king."

Then the angel disappeared as he had done before.

Columba rubbed his eyes. "I do not like this dreaming," he said. "I sit too long over my books and grow overtired, so fall to dreaming. I must go earlier to my bed."

But through the day he felt ill at ease. He chided himself for letting a dream disturb him, and tried to console himself by saying that it was commonly said of dreams that they went by contraries, in which case his choice was right.

That night he left his books unopened and sought his bed early. Then for the third time the angel came and standing at the side of the bed, held the open book before

Columba's eyes. The light that shone from the letters of Aidan's name lit the hut as brightly as if a dozen tapers burned. But Columba shook his head and cried out stubbornly, "My choice is made. I will not have Aidan! Eoghan shall be king."

Then light flamed from the wings of the angel and from the crystal book with a white brilliance so blinding that Columba was forced to cover his eyes with his arms. For the first time the angel spoke.

"Foolish man!" he thundered. "Aidan, not Eoghan, shall be king!" and raising his hand he struck Columba upon his side with such violence that Columba fell back senseless upon his bed.

In the morning Columba, upon rising, felt a pain so sharp that he looked to see what caused it. Like a scar upon his side he saw plainly the mark of the angel's fingers. Then he realized that he had not been dreaming. "Glory be to God!" he cried. "He has saved me from error. 'Twas an angel sent down from Heaven against whom I have been striving these three nights!"

That same day he sent for Aidan and, when he came, consecrating him, ordained him as king.

Columba thus was brought to realize that his mistake had been in not understanding that Aidan's heat and passion were the marks of the man's strength. It was a strong man who was needed to rule the country, not one like Eoghan, so little inclined to effort that he would let his ambassadors make his decisions for him.

To those who were surprised at his choice, Columba said only, "Ah, well, 'I will' is not always God's will."

But to the end of his days he bore the marks of the angel's fingers on his side.

hen MacBeth of Moray slew King Duncan of Scotland and set himself up to be king in Duncan's stead, the friends of Duncan were greatly troubled about the safety of Duncan's two young sons. They knew that MacBeth would not be likely to allow the princes to remain alive after he became king, so they got hold of them and carried them out of the country to the court of Edward, the English king.

King Malcolm III 1067 A.D.

The sons of Duncan were received kindly by Edward, who took them into his own care and had them brought up at his court as wards of the Crown. They were so carefully guarded and protected that MacBeth could never have got at them to harm them, even if he had dared to try.

When Malcolm, the older son, came to manhood he began to think it was time for him to try to get back the kingdom that should have been his, if MacBeth had not killed his father to get it. Malcolm had lived in exile at the English court for fifteen years, and although he had been as carefree and happy as any child could be, he never forgot that he was not English, but Scottish, and that he had been born to be Scotland's king.

His childhood days were over now. He knew he wasn't going to get the crown by asking for it. If he was going to have to fight MacBeth for it, and he didn't know any other way of going about it, the sooner he started the better. Because first of all, he'd have to find an army.

Malcolm had never had any trouble making friends, but it came as a surprise to him that he had so many that were ready to help him now. And to his English allies was added one whose aid he had never expected.

Siward, the great and powerful Danish Earl of Northumbria, sent word that he would come into the fight on Malcolm's side.

Siward had a very good reason for wanting to overthrow MacBeth. Crinan, Duncan's father and Malcolm's grandfather, had also been slain by MacBeth. Crinan had been a close connection of Siward's, by marriage, and it was a matter of family honor to Siward that Mac-Beth be punished for Crinan's death. Siward would be doubly happy if it was Malcolm, Crinan's grandson, who took the crown of Scotland away from MacBeth.

Then, one after another, the Scottish earls and barons who had been friends of Duncan's let Malcolm know that they were ready to join him. So when Malcolm marched into Scotland he had a sizable army of Scottish and English soldiers, while the Danish Earl Siward had already gone on before him to open the fighting with his Danes.

Wars are not won in a day or in one battle. It took three years before they put an end to MacBeth. Then they had to contend with Lulach, MacBeth's successor. But Malcolm's English and Scottish army, aided by Siward and his Danes, were victorious at last. Malcolm, so long the English exile, became King Malcolm III of Scotland.

When he came into his kingdom Malcolm did not forget his allies. The Danish Earl Siward considered himself rewarded when Crinan's death was avenged, and withdrew to Northumbria, very well satisfied. But Malcolm kept in his mind the memory that it was the English who had sheltered him for the years of his exile, and helped him fight for the Scottish crown. When, some years after he had returned to Scotland as king, his English friends needed his help, he was happy to be of service to them.

William, Duke of Normandy, came over to England with his army and, conquering the country, seized the crown and made himself King of England. Many of the English nobles, fearing that death or imprisonment would be their fate if the Normans laid hands upon them, fled to Scotland to seek refuge there.

Malcolm at once ordered that all who came were to be received with courtesy and kindness by the Scottish people. If the newcomers knew no friends in Scotland with whom they might find homes, lodging was to be found for them, and they were to be provided with such help as they might need.

Not only the English nobles, but churchmen, merchants, and men who had been of importance in England, came pouring into Scotland, bringing with them their families and such things of value as they had been able to gather up in their flight. But there were some who had no possessions at all, other than the clothes they wore. A few slipped over the border between England and Scotland, but a much greater number came by sea.

Hardly a ship came into a Scottish port that did not bring with it a number of these English exiles, fleeing from the tyrannies of the new Norman king.

Beyond making sure that shelter was found for them and that they did not come to want, there was little that

Malcolm could do for them. He had a sum of money from the treasury put for their use and appointed trustworthy men to handle their affairs. He knew that if there were any of his friends whom he had known in England, or

any who had helped him in his fight, among the exiles, they would come straight to him at the castle without waiting to be asked. They knew they'd find a hearty welcome there. As for the rest, there were too many of them, and his time was too taken up with the business of running Scotland, for him to be able to follow the fortunes of all of them himself.

It happened one day that as Malcolm sat in his castle, busy with the castle accounts, with his chief steward by his side, a messenger came to tell him that a ship was just coming into the harbor bearing upon her deck a great number of people who, by their dress, appeared to be English.

The king was not too pleased at being interrupted while at work on a busy morning. There were many important things to be decided, and a ship from England was nothing new. But, being a kind and patient man, Malcolm put his work by for the moment, and sent for his buidealair, the head of the castle staff of servants.

When he came, Malcolm told him he had just had word that a ship was coming in with a large company of English on board. It seemed that the folk at the harbor were, for some reason, disturbed by it, so would the buidealair just go down to the harbor, and welcome the people to the country, and make sure that they were taken care of in the town.

Soon the man came running back, all out of breath, and excited about the ship. It was just coming into the

harbor now, he told the king, and his Majesty would
have to forgive him, but his Majesty would understand,
if he were to see the people on board the ship. "The lot
of them are so richly clad and bear themselves so proud,"
he said, "that I feel myself too humble to receive them. *The Tale of*
Will your Majesty not send someone grander than me?" *the Royal*
he begged. *Exiles*

"Och!" said the king impatiently. Then, with a sigh,
he said to his steward, "I can ill spare you, but what
needs be, must be! Go you down yourself and bid these
fine folk welcome."

So the steward went down to meet the strangers, while
the king went on with his work by himself.

Very shortly the steward came running back to King
Malcolm, out of breath and full of excitement, too. The
ship had come into the harbor and was just about to cast
anchor, but the steward would like to be excused, if his
Majesty pleased, from receiving the company who had
come on the ship.

"For elegance and proud bearing, their like has never
been seen, your Majesty," the steward told him. "I
wouldn't know what to say to them, they're all so rich
and fine. Then I have little English and I doubt they'd
make much out of my Scottish speech."

"Bother!" exclaimed the king.

"Pray, let your Majesty send someone else instead of
me," begged the steward.

"Ah, well," sighed the king. "I'll go then myself."

So King Malcolm left his castle and went down to the
shore.

When he got there the fugitives were just coming
down from the ship and Malcolm could understand the

reluctance the buidealair and the steward had felt. The exiles that day were very great people indeed. They were the members of the royal family from England with a large retinue of servants they'd brought along. It was only fitting, King Malcolm said to himself, that a king should welcome the family of a king.

There were Prince Aedgar Aethling, and with him his mother Queen Agatha, his two sisters, Christina and Margaret, the Earls Marleswain and Gospatrick and many other good nobles, their squires and gillies, as well as a number of maidservants to wait upon the queen and the princesses. In number the company came to about three score.

Their faces showed the anxieties caused by the hazards of the voyage and the perils of the flight, and King Malcolm's heart turned toward them warmly, for they were exiles now in his country, but he remembered the years he had spent as an exile himself, at their own court. So he welcomed them all with great courtesy and kindness and bade them consider his castle their home for as long as they cared to stay. And he offered his hand in friendship to each of his royal guests in turn.

When he came to Princess Margaret and, taking her hand in his own, looked into her face, he was so struck by her beauty, and by the simplicity and gentleness of her manner, that he could find no words to say to her at all.

Seeing his confusion, the English princess smiled up at the Scottish king. In that moment he lost his heart to her, and to the end of his life, he never got it back again.

But, for the moment, he kept her hand in his own, and led her back to the castle, while the rest of the com-

pany followed in stately procession, according to their rank.

"The Fairest Flower of England"—that was what King Malcolm always called Margaret. Before the year was over he had won her heart, so they were married and she became Scotland's queen.

And many a time he was heard to say that his happiness began on the day he left his work and went down to the harbor to welcome a shipload of exiles, and found his princess there.

Robert Bruce
1306 A.D.

he Scots once had a king that they had little use for. He was a puppet of King Edward I of England who had chosen him for the post, and he had to dance the way the English king pulled the strings. John Baliol, his name was, but the Scottish people called him Toom-Tabard, or Empty-Coat, meaning there was no one inside the royal robes he wore, because he was no good to them as a king at all.

After a few years Toom-Tabard got tired of taking the orders of the English king, so he gathered an army together and rebelled against him. But Baliol's army was so small, and that of the English king so large, that it was no time at all before he lost the rebellion, and his plight was worse than it had been before.

By that time Toom-Tabard decided that being king of Scotland was too much trouble so he gave it up. He packed his belongings and started for France, taking along with him the royal crown and scepter which he thought, very likely, they'd not be needing any more, and a large sum of money which he'd managed to get hold of before he left.

Edward's men caught up with him and found the things he'd taken, hidden among his clothes. The English king took the crown and the scepter away from him, but kindly allowed him to keep the money, no doubt hoping he'd use it to travel as far away from Scotland as he could.

Now Scotland had no king and Edward I was delighted to have things turning out so well for himself. He planned to add Scotland to England, making one country of the two, twice as big as England had been before. Of course he planned to be king of it all himself.

To keep the Scottish nobles under his thumb, he made them all come to swear fealty to him. When they came, they found he'd prepared a paper for them to sign. Every earl or baron or landholder who had estates or castles must put his name down on the list. If anyone's name was missing, the owner would be considered an outlaw, and his lands would be taken away.

More than two thousand Scottish earls and lords signed this Ragman's Roll, as it was called by the Scots. But many of them signed it thinking, "You may be king today, Your Majesty, but have a care for tomorrow!" The ink was scarcely dry before some of them were planning to chase the English out of Scotland and make Scotland free again.

But for a while the Scots had a sorry time of it. An English governor was put over the country and Englishmen filled all the important positions in all the land. The king even took some of the castles from the Scottish earls who owned them and gave them to English friends of his own. Because they did not want to lose their lands or be put into prison the Scots appeared to submit to these injustices, but under the surface there was trouble brewing.

The first rebellion was started by William Wallace, a great-hearted gentleman who was devoted to his country. He might have won in the end, for he was too stubborn

to give up the fight, even when he met reverses. But one
of his own countrymen, tempted by a large reward
offered for his capture, betrayed him into the hands of
the English and he was seized and taken to London,
where the king had him beheaded.

That, thought King Edward, will be the last of my
trouble with the Scots. He spoke too soon, for among
the Scottish earls who had been admitted to his court,
and appeared to be on good terms with him were two
who, when they signed the Ragman's Roll, must have
crossed the fingers of their left hands behind their back.

Sir John Comyn, commonly called the Red Comyn,
because of his flaming red hair, was one of these. He was
not only a member of the great and rich family of the
Comyns, but through the marriage of his father to the
sister of John Baliol, the former king, a possible claimant to the Scottish throne.

Robert Bruce, the other claimant, was Earl of Carrick
and Lord of Annandale, and possessed great estates both
on Scottish soil and in England. His fortune was enormous and he had many followers whom he could call to
his side. He considered his title to the throne of Scotland
was better than Comyn's because he was one generation
nearer their ancestor, Alexander III. Perhaps, better
than any claim he might make, was Bruce's own determination to be king of Scotland.

However, the English king was sure that he held Scotland like a bird in his hand. Toom-Tabard had made it
plain that he had no intention of coming back again.
England's greatest Scottish enemy, William Wallace,
was dead. As for the Scottish earls, they seemed to accept

Edward's directions without making too much fuss about them. Everything was going well. That's what the English king thought.

But, in secret, Robert Bruce was busy among the Scottish earls. A league was being formed among them with the purpose of rising against the English and ridding the country of them once and for all. The disposition of the Scottish people had been so severely tried by the invaders that they were ready to follow any leader who would attempt to drive the English out. Bruce felt that, with the earls to lead them, the people would rush to the standard in such numbers that they could not fail to win their cause.

The one person about whom Bruce was uneasy was Red Comyn. Since he and Bruce both claimed the right to be king of Scotland, it was not likely that Comyn would be willing to help his rival to gain the throne. But the ill-will between Bruce and Comyn had existed long before John Baliol had given up the crown. There was an ancient enmity between the families of Bruce and Comyn, and added to that, they disliked each other so heartily that, since boyhood, there had seldom been a meeting between them that did not end in a fight.

After thinking the matter over for some time, Bruce decided it would be best to go to Comyn and tell him that the Scottish earls were considering the formation of a league with the intention of freeing Scotland and putting a Scottish king on the throne. This he did, giving enough information that Comyn might understand that the chance of success was good, but being careful not to mention the names of the conspirators, since his distrust of Comyn was so deep.

Comyn listened in silence until Bruce had finished. Then he said, "It sounds very well. Pray, tell me. Who will be king of this kingdom, when you have set it up?"

Bruce had expected that question, and had an answer ready for it.

"The choice lies between you and me," he said. "No one else can claim a right to be king. But I see no sense in fighting for it when it can be settled in peace. If you will give to me your lands and your castles, I will not contest your right to be king, and will give you what help I can. Or, if you prefer, take all of my estates, and let me be king."

Comyn took time to think it over, but finally told Bruce that he had rather take Bruce's estates, and Bruce could be king if he liked. At Bruce's insistence, Comyn promised not to tell King Edward about the conspiracy and the bargain he and Bruce had made.

Bruce, because of the affairs of his English estates, was often in London. He returned there soon after he had talked to Red Comyn, and as, at the time, he was in the favor of the English king, he was often at court, where he had many friends.

Very early one morning, several weeks after he had come down from Scotland, the Earl of Gloucester's manservant came to Bruce, bringing him a deerskin pouch. His master, the man said, had found it in his room after Bruce had been to see him the night before. The earl had instructed his servant to return the pouch to Bruce at once, as he thought it might be of great importance to him.

Bruce knew that the pouch did not belong to him, but he accepted it, and after the servant had left, he opened it to see what it held. To his surprise there was nothing in it but a spur and a silver coin.

The Earl of Gloucester was Bruce's cousin and a very close friend. He was a quiet, serious man, and Bruce

knew that he would not have sent these things in jest. There must be some hidden meaning to them.

"A riddle!" Bruce exclaimed, "and I must find the answer."

He laid the coin and the spur on his writing table, and drawing up a chair, he sat down before them to figure the riddle out.

Bruce was quick-witted, and it did not take him long. The Earl of Gloucester, learning that Bruce was in danger, had taken this means to let him know, since he dared not come himself, lest he be suspected of warning Bruce.

Spurs were used to make a horse go at the greatest possible speed. And as Bruce turned the coin in his fingers, the face of King Edward, stamped on the coin, looked back at him.

So that was the meaning of the Earl of Gloucester's riddle. Bruce was in danger from King Edward, and must take to his horse and get away as fast as he could. He wasted no time, but quickly summoned his companions who had come with him from Scotland, and bade them ride out at once, taking different directions so that their departure from the castle would not be noticed. They should meet together again at the end of the town, and await his arrival there. After he had made sure that they had got away safely and without interference, Bruce had his own horse saddled. He rode out in a care-

less, unhurried manner, as if he were going out for a morning's pleasure in the town.

But once well away from the palace, Bruce spurred up his horse and rode at top speed to join his friends at the appointed meeting place. Then all of them galloped off, as fast as their horses could take them, up the road that led northward toward Scotland.

As they came to the Border, they met a messenger riding post-haste toward London, and Bruce recognized him as one of the followers of Comyn who often employed him to carry out his secret affairs. Setting himself in the messenger's way, Bruce ordered him to stop and tell whence he came and where he was going. The fellow refused to answer any questions, or to account for himself, but suddenly drawing his sword, rode at Bruce to attack him. Bruce's companions came to his aid and in the ensuing fight, Comyn's man was slain.

When Bruce examined the dispatch case carried by the messenger he learned how great had been the danger from which he had escaped. From the papers in the case, he learned that Comyn had already broken his promise and had sent word some days before to the king about the bargain he and Bruce had made. The documents the slain man had been taking to London gave proof of the part Bruce had played in the plot to free Scotland. The king had been biding his time until the papers arrived from Comyn, when he intended to have Bruce seized and put in prison to await trial.

Now that the papers were in Bruce's hands he promptly destroyed them, burning them by the side of the road. As he rode on into Scotland he realized that only by a spur and a coin and a loyal friend had he been saved from falling into Comyn's trap.

Now he saw clearly what Comyn's purpose had been. The king would have had Bruce beheaded, as he had had William Wallace. Then, with Bruce dead, Comyn would have no obstacle between himself and the Scottish throne, and would have possession of all of Bruce's estates as well.

Bruce hurried to make use of what time he had to warn all Scotland to prepare for war. Since Edward knew that the Scottish people were planning to rise against him, he would be marching against Scotland very soon, to put the rebellion down. But whether ready or not, the Scottish earls and barons could count upon their followers whenever there was a war to fight, because the love of fighting was bred in their blood and their bones. In the case of this war, when the prize was the freedom of Scotland, there would not be one laggard in the land.

As for Red Comyn, Bruce went himself to settle with him. As in the past, their meeting ended in a furious quarrel. It was their last one, for in the course of it Red Comyn was slain.

It was never known surely if Bruce was responsible for his death, or if he was slain by one of Bruce's friends who had come with him, but it raised a storm which Bruce had to weather for many a year. Only by his great devotion to Scotland, and the courage and the ability he showed during the war, was he able to atone for Comyn's death.

So it might be said that the great war for Scottish

independence began with the riddle of a spur and a coin. Eight years passed after Bruce met Comyn's messenger at the Scottish Border before the last battle was fought at Bannockburn. Bruce and his Scots won that battle, and Bruce came into his kingdom at last.

No Scottish king, before or after, loved his country and his people so dearly, nor served them so faithfully and well. And no Scottish king was ever loved so greatly by the people over whom he ruled.

ohn, Lord of the Western Isles, had a son named Angus, a hot-headed lad, quick to avenge a slight or an insult and always spoiling for a fight. Angus, though young, was already a man of some importance, being chieftain of the Isle of Islay and the son-in-law of the rich and powerful Earl of Argyll. But in spite of it all he was not satisfied.

Angus of Islay 1480 A.D.

His father, the Lord of the Isles, had formerly been the Earl of Ross as well. But the estates of Ross and Kintyre were on the mainland and the Isles were enough for John to look after, so he had ceded all his lands of Ross and Kintyre to the Scottish king while Angus was still a small child.

Now that Angus was grown to manhood, he got it into his head that these estates belonged to the family and ought to be returned. In a very high-handed fashion he sent a petition to the king, demanding that the lands be given to him, as son of the Lord of the Isles, since his father did not care to be burdened with them. The king only laughed at Angus, and told him he had no intention of parting with the estates.

This put Angus into a fine temper. "Very well!" said he. "If the king is not disposed to give me back the land that is mine by right, I'll take it back myself."

The Lord of the Isles was greatly disturbed to hear that Angus threatened to seize Ross. Ever since he was born, Angus had been up to some mischief or other, and he showed no signs of improvement as he grew older. The lad had been no comfort at all to his father in the past, and now he could very well be a danger to him. If Angus marched into Ross with his men and tried to take it by force of arms, the Lord of the Isles was afraid the king would hold it against the father as well as the son.

He tried to reason with Angus, but he might as well have saved his breath to cool his porridge.

"You'll be wise to remember, Angus," said the Lord of the Isles. "It wasn't the king that was asking for the lands. I gave them up to him of my own free will, to do him a favor, like. 'Twas all my own doing."

"Then the more fool, you!" Angus replied angrily. "You gave up what you should have kept for me, since you did not want it yourself!"

"That is all as it may be," said the Lord of the Isles. "It's done now, and past undoing. And if you'll take a word of advice from me, which most like you will not, you'd better put yourself on the good side of the king by letting the matter drop entirely. One of these days you'll go too far, and what could you do against the king, with all the earls of Scotland and their armies behind him?"

But there was no reasoning with Angus. Ross he must have, and Ross he would have. And when at last his father threatened to stop him by having him held prisoner in his own castle, Angus came back at his father by declaring war against him.

So the father and the son fought it out, but it was all of no use, for the men of the Isles were defeated by Angus in a great battle between their ships. The battle was fought in a bay near Tobermory, and the fighting was so fierce that the waters of the sea ran red that day with the blood of dead warriors. Ever since that battle has been known as the Battle of the Bloody Bay.

At that, the Lord of the Isles gave up in despair, for he saw that he could do no more. He sailed back home with what was left of his army and washed his hands of his headstrong son and all his doings, forever after.

After he had settled with his father, Angus was so full of himself that he thought he was twice as big a man as he had been before. He gathered together his army and went over to Ross. Up and down Ross he swept, raiding and pillaging, laying hold of villages, towns and castles. The people of Ross fled into the neighboring lands and left their own to Angus and his men.

But the victory over his father and the raids on Ross brought Angus no closer to getting Ross for his own. It made so much trouble for Angus that in the end he lost everything he had won.

As his father had warned him, the Scottish king was ill-pleased to hear about the misdeeds of the son of the Lord of the Isles. It was plain to be seen that his father could not control him so the king sent for the Earl of Atholl and the Earl of Argyll, the latter being Angus's father-in-law. When they came to him, he told them the rebel chieftain was getting too big for his boots, in his opinion.

"He'll have to be stopped, and the sooner, the better," the king said to the earls, "or he'll be getting entirely out of hand." How they went about it, he left to them, but he gave orders that the two of them were to make sure that Angus of Islay was taken down a peg or two.

Either one of the earls could call up a hundred men for every ten that were in the command of Angus.

Neither one was unwilling, for Angus had managed to give them both plenty of grievances against him. So they went home and assembled their armies and marched against Angus and his Islaymen.

It didn't take long for the two earls to clear Angus out of Ross entirely. He and his men took to their boats and hurried back home to Islay, and there Angus stayed for a while, fuming and fretting, and promising himself that, one fine day, he'd get even with Argyll and Atholl and pay them back for chasing him out of Ross.

Then the Earl of Atholl made a move that roused Angus to a new pitch of fury. The Earl thought it would be well to have a hostage to ensure Angus's good behavior in the future, so he made a secret journey to Islay and carried away the little son of Angus. Atholl carried the child to its grandfather, the Earl of Argyll, and left it in his care. Argyll placed the babe in his fortified castle at Lochawe, surrounding it with trusted attendants, and setting plenty of guards about it to keep it in safety from its father, should he attempt to get it back again. The earl thought Angus no fit person to have charge of the upbringing of his grandchild.

Although Angus was angry enough at his father-in-law for accepting the child, the full fury of his wrath was directed against the Earl of Atholl, who had stolen his child from him. He assembled a fleet of galleys and gathering together all his fighting men, he sailed from Islay to the mainland, bent upon punishing Atholl. Invading the earl's estates, everything that would burn they set fire to, plundering as they went along.

The Earl of Atholl, surprised by the sudden attack, had no time to gather his army to help him. He fled with his countess to the church of Saint Bride, where they sought sanctuary. They should have been safe there, for by the law of sanctuary, any person seeking refuge in a church must not be touched or harmed. It was considered that they were under the protection of God, and the penalty for breaking this law was excommunication from the church. Angus, in his rage, paid no heed to the law. Rushing into the church, he dragged the earl and his countess out, and made them prisoners.

The priest of Saint Bride's church, outraged by the wicked deed, followed Angus out. Pronouncing the penalty of excommunication upon him, he laid a curse upon the chieftain of Islay.

"Thou shalt be cursed in all thy doings, Angus of Islay!" the priest shouted after him. "Thou shalt be cursed in thy comings and in thy goings, at home and abroad, by land and by sea!"

But Angus turned his back on the priest, and he and his men went off, carrying with them the rich loot they had stolen from the houses they had burned in the raid, and taking with them the Earl and the Countess of Atholl, who now despaired of their lives.

The plunder was loaded into the galleys, and Angus took his captives into the ship in which he meant to sail himself. The fleet started out to return to Islay, and Angus was well pleased with his revenge, and he eyed the despairing earl and countess with a satisfaction which he did not attempt to conceal.

They had gone no more than half the way to Islay when the heavens split with a thunderous crash, and a great gale came tearing down upon them, with blinding torrents of hail and rain. Many of the galleys sank under

the force of the storm, and the stolen treasure they bore
was lost forever in the depths of the sea. The lightning
pursued Angus, striking before and behind him, as if it
sought to destroy him, and his men began to cry out that
God in his wrath had sent the storm against them to
punish them for invading the sanctuary of the church.

Angus, in terror, shouted to his captain to turn the
ship and return at once to Atholl.

"I can stand against my father and the Earls of Atholl
and Argyll," he cried out in despair, "and I could stand
against the king. But I cannot stand against the wrath
of God!"

And as the ship, retracing its course, started back to
Atholl, the storm ceased as suddenly as it had begun.
Under a clear, calm night sky the ship reached the shore.
There, with careful courtesy, Angus released the Earl
and the Countess of Atholl, and leading them from the
galley, let them, without hindrance, find their way back
to their castle through their ruined lands.

That same night Angus and his men, barefoot and clad
only in their shirts, without swords and armor, returned
to the church of Saint Bride. They stood humbly before
the door, begging to be allowed to enter. When at last
they were admitted, they cast themselves down before
the altar. There, for three long days and three long
nights, they lay beseeching Heaven in its mercy to forgive them, and release them from the wrath of God.

When at last the ban of the church was lifted, and
Angus and his men went back to Islay, he went back
without his son. In solemn council, the Scottish king,
the Western Earls, and even the Lord of the Isles,
decided that it would be well for the babe to remain with

his grandfather, the Earl of Argyll. Angus paid high for his feuds and his battles and for the ruin of Atholl. He never saw his son again.

It was a good thing, for his repentance was not long-lasting. Although he did not trouble Atholl or Ross, soon his temper found other targets to hurl itself against. He went from bad to worse, until even his own people could no longer bear him. In two or three years he was slain by the men of his own clan. No one mourned him but his father, whom he had treated so badly, and so ended the short and wicked life of Angus, son of the Lord of the Isles.

THE TALE OF A DEBT REPAID

The Earl of Sutherland 1487 A.D.

The custom of hospitality was well-established in Scotland in ancient times. There were hard and fast rules which governed its practice, and every man was taught them in his childhood and respected them all the rest of his life. No man seeking shelter could be refused. Even if the person claiming hospitality was an enemy, he must be taken in, and between sundown and sunrise, he was safe from harm. His host was bound to protect him during those hours, but the guest also had responsibilities of his own. If, while he was accepting hospitality, his host should be attacked, it was the duty of his guest to come to his aid, to defend him if need should arise, even with his own life.

Uilleam Dhu Aberigh of the clan of the MacKays once had very good cause to thank God that, in his case, the laws of hospitality were faithfully kept.

In those days, the clan of the MacKays were often in a state of feud with the Sutherland clan, and fighting broke out between them again and again.

Ian Aberigh, the father of Uilleam Dhu was acting as *toiseach*, or leader, of the MacKays while the chief of that clan was being detained at Perth during the king's pleasure. Ian led the clan out against the Sutherlands to settle one of their differences, and naturally Uilleam Dhu came along with his father.

The MacKays got the best of the argument that day, and before the day was over, the Sutherland men gave up the field and ran for home. The MacKays, happy and victorious, started homeward, too, after the battle was over, but somehow or other, young Uilleam Dhu became separated from his companions, and, while trying to find his way back to them, got himself lost in a region unknown to him.

As he went along trying to get himself on the right road again he met with two men of the Sutherlands, also on their way home, and both of them greatly annoyed by the way the battle had gone against them.

When they set eyes on young Uilleam Dhu, they saw at once, by his tartan, that he was one of the clan of MacKay, and, to some measure at least, responsible for the Sutherland defeat. So they waylaid him, and drawing their swords, hurled themselves upon him, intending to take his life.

Although there were two of the Sutherlands, and Uilleam Dhu was alone, he resolved to sell his life as early as possible. With his own sword he made at them with such fire and spirit that he was able to hold them off. One of the two was slain in the fight and Uilleam managed to escape from the other by plunging deep into the forest that bordered the road.

There he wandered about in the dusk, trying first one way then another. To his discomfort rain began falling, and the mists of evening rose about him, further hindering him in his attempt to find a road which would lead him home.

The sun had long set and the wet night was black about him before his stumbling feet felt a road beneath them at last. He kept to the track as well as he could, going by feeling rather than sight, until the road ended

at a clearing in which stood a house or lodge of some sort. In the darkness he could not tell what its size was, or its appearance, but he knew that it was occupied, for through the window, the wooden blinds of which were

fastened back, he could see firelight dancing upon the walls within, reflected from a fire which burned upon the hearth.

In answer to his knock, a man came to the door and, when Uilleam Dhu asked for shelter, bade him enter. The room into which he was taken was lit only by the fire, but as his host leaned over the hearth to add fresh fuel to the coals, the flames blazed up and for a minute Uilleam Dhu saw the man's face clearly, and recognized him as none other than the Earl of Sutherland, whose forces had been routed by the MacKays that day. Hardly had Uilleam settled himself upon a bench in a darker corner away from the fire, when he heard the sound of feet running toward the house. Presently a voice hailed the earl, who left the room and, opening the door, went out.

Uilleam could hear voices, but could make no sense of what was said until the earl, about to come into the house, paused on the doorstep and said, "Nay, let it be. The deed is done and cannot be undone. There has been enough trouble in this day, without seeking more in the wet and dark of the night. It might well turn out to be a fool's errand besides. Let it be until the morn."

Then the men went away, muttering their dissatisfaction, and the earl came back into the room.

"I shall be but poor company for you," he said heavily. "I have just had word of the death of a young cousin whom my heart held dear. He was slain this night by one of the MacKays."

Then Uilleam Dhu Aberigh started up from the bench upon which he sat. "I am that MacKay who slew thy kinsman. Had I known this was your house I should not have sought shelter here. And if he died at my hands, know that it was in fair combat he fell, and the odds against me were two to one." And when the earl did not reply at once Uilleam Dhu added, "If you would like your revenge, sir, you shall have it."

Then the earl answered. "I knew well who you were, Uilleam Dhu, son of Ian Aberigh, when you came to my door. I did not know that my cousin had died by your hands, but if I had known, 'twould have been the same. You asked for shelter and I could not refuse. Never shall it be said that the ancient laws of hospitality were broken by a Sutherland. Put up your sword! We shall not fight tonight."

Then he set food and drink before Uilleam Dhu, and quoting the old Gaelic saying, *"Biadh an diugh, agus cogadh am mairéach*—Food today and feud tomorrow." He bade him eat.

When Uilleam Dhu had eaten, the earl told him, "Lay yourself down, now, and rest. You will be safe, for I myself will keep watch while you sleep."

So Uilleam Dhu stretched himself upon a bench near the fire, and wearied after his day, soon fell asleep, while his enemy kept guard.

When the night had begun to turn toward day again, with perhaps two hours or a little more before dawn, the earl roused Uilleam Dhu from his sleep and told him it was time for him to be on his way.

With great courtesy, the earl himself led Uilleam through the forest to the boundary of the Sutherland lands. He set Uilleam on the road and pointed out to him the direction in which he must travel to reach his home.

Then said the earl, "Be on your way, Uilleam, son of Ian Aberigh! Be on your way, Uilleam Dhu! You are safe from me until the rising of the sun, but take warning. With the sun's first ray the Sutherlands will be after you, to hunt you out if we can." And without another word, he turned and vanished into the forest from which they had just come.

Uilleam Dhu, refreshed by food and rest, went speedily on, and soon reached country with which he was familiar, and made his way home with no further mishap.

Soon or late, feuds come to their ends. The trouble between the MacKays and the Sutherlands was caused for the most part by quarrels about land boundaries, and before long these had been settled and the two clans were at peace together.

Six years after the night Uilleam Dhu lost himself in the forest and was sheltered by the Earl of Sutherland, the MacKays had started a new feud, this time with the Earl of Ross.

The feud was not concerned with boundaries but had a more serious origin. Angus Mackay had been slain when ambushed by a party of men from Ross and the Clan MacKay had three serious counts against his murderers. In the first place, Angus was the son of Neill, chief of the Clan MacKay. In the second place, he had been peaceably engaged in hunting when he was attacked. And furthermore, he had been killed on land belonging to the MacKays, upon which the men of Ross were trespassing at the time.

The Clan MacKay demanded that the murderers be surrendered to them for punishment, but as two of them were closely related to the Earl of Ross, he refused to give them up. So, with a cause so just, the Clan MacKay did not hesitate to declare war against Ross. Clan Mac-Kay called out not only their own clansmen, but all their allies who were willing to join in the fight to avenge the death of Angus MacKay.

The peace between the Sutherlands and the Mackays was so well established by this time that the Earl of Sutherland sent a body of five hundred men, under the command of his uncle Robert Sutherland to fight beside the MacKays.

The clans of Ross paid dearly for the slaying of Angus MacKay. The victory was so complete that when the fighting was over the lands of Ross were a smoking ruin, and the chief of Ross with a good dozen of his best leaders lay dead on the battlefield. The plunder gathered from the vanquished territory was so vast that it was said to have the value of a king's ransom. It was divided, share and share alike, among the victors. Then the leaders withdrew with their men, each group to its own encampment, to rest from the battle before returning to their homes.

The men of Assunth, a division of the MacKays, were gathered together under the leadership of Eoghan Rhiab-haich. Cruel and greedy by nature, Rhiabhaich cast his roving eye on the share of the plunder that fell to the

Sutherland men, and coveted it so greatly that he could see no reason why he and his men should not have it as well as their own.

It came into his mind that if he waited until night had well set in and the Sutherlands were at rest and unsuspecting, he and his men could steal into their camp and slay them while they slept. Then the Assunthmen could take the Sutherland's share of the plunder and add it to their own. When Robert Sutherland and his men did not come home, the Earl of Sutherland would take it for granted that all of them had perished in the battle against Ross.

Partly by persuasion and partly by threats, Rhiabhaich won the consent of his men to his plan. He and his men remained in their camp to wait through the remaining hours of the day.

That same Uilleam Dhu Aberigh who, six years before, had sought shelter from the Earl of Sutherland, had come along with the Aberighs to fight with the MacKays. By chance, he learned about the plot of Eoghan Rhiabhaich against the Sutherland men.

Uilleam Dhu was horrified by the brutality and the treachery of Rhiabhaich. And he had in his mind, too, the old memory of the night that the Earl of Sutherland had not given him away, when his men had come to tell him of his kinsman's death, nor had he sought to avenge it himself, abiding by the old law of hospitality.

"I owe much to the Earl of Sutherland," said Uilleam Dhu to himself. "But to Eoghan Rhiabhaich I owe naught at all." Besides, the Sutherlands had come out to aid the MacKays in a quarrel which, after all, was not their own.

So Uilleam Dhu determined to prevent the slaughter

of the Sutherlands. Straightway he went to Robert Sutherland, and told him of Rhiabhaich's intention, warning him to be on his guard that night.

"We'll do better than that," said Robert Sutherland grimly. "We'll not be here at all!"

Robert Sutherland quickly gathered his men together and told them what Rhiabhaich planned to do. The best way to forestall his treachery and disappoint the traitor would be for the Sutherland men to get themselves out of his way at once. To this, his men were all in hearty agreement.

Within the hour, Robert Sutherland led his men off, in close formation, with the treasure in the midst of their ranks. Rhiabhaich beheld them marching away and was filled with amazement and consternation. They must have been warned, he knew, but could not guess who the informer had been. He dared not stop them, nor attack them openly, with all the forces of the MacKays ready to take their part against him. There was nothing at all that he could do now, but stand and watch them go.

Uilleam Dhu also watched the Sutherlands march away. There was a time, thought he, when he had killed one of the Earl of Sutherland's kinsmen, and in spite of it, the earl had spared his life. Well, then for the life that he had taken, that night six years ago, he had returned to the Earl this day his uncle and all his men, all alive and unharmed.

Uilleam Dhu was contented. He had long owed a debt to the Earl of Sutherland, and now the debt was paid.

The Earl
of Argyll
1527 A.D.

The Earl of Argyll had a bonny young sister, and her name was the Lady Elizabeth. Lachlan Cattanach MacLean of Duart wooed her and won her and carried her off to his island home as his bride.

Lady Elizabeth soon found out she'd made a mistake in her choice of a husband. Lachlan MacLean was haughty, selfish, and arrogant beyond believing. He was the sort of man who only wanted a thing until he got it, and once it was in his possession, he set no store by it at all. And, worst of all, he was greedy for money and gear. Although the Lady Elizabeth had brought him a very respectable dowry, he thought it should have been bigger, and did not mind letting her know how he felt.

The Lady Elizabeth was meek and gentle by nature. She made no protest when her husband was unkind, not that it would have helped matters any if she had. But with a man who was always brooding in silence, or telling her how much better off he'd be without her, she had very little to be happy about.

It was not very long before Lachlan MacLean began casting his eye about, looking over the unmarried daughters on the neighboring islands, and figuring out in his mind how much bigger their marriage portions would be than the one he had got with the Lady Elizabeth. There was one lass in particular that took his fancy. Strange to tell, she was a cousin of his own, and he couldn't see how he had missed her when he was looking about for a wife. She dwelt with her father on the nearby isle of Treshinish, and she was lively and pretty, which was well enough, in its way, but what really interested him was that he had found out that she was also a great heiress, which Lachlan MacLean thought was much better than any amount of charm and wit.

It never occurred to him to wonder if his cousin on Treshinish would have wanted him for a husband. Having a very good opinion of his worth, although he had very little to base it upon, he was convinced that she'd have been happy to take him, if he'd asked her instead of the Earl of Argyll's sister, when he was thinking of getting wed.

Now it was just his mischance that, whether she'd take him or not, she couldn't have him, for what could a man do when he already had a wife? He'd have gone off like a shot to Treshinish to ask his cousin to marry him, but the Lady Elizabeth stood in his way.

It wouldn't do just to send his wife back to her brother and say that he didn't want to keep her. If he did that, he'd have to be sending back the dowry she'd brought him, and he couldn't bear to part with that. The Earl of Argyll was a man of great power, forbye. He had kinsmen and friends by the thousands at his beck and call, and if he chose to take offense at having his sister returned to him, he could very well start a feud about it, and that would be the end of Lachlan Cattanach MacLean.

Between Duart and the mainland, near the lonely end of Lismore, there was a great rock in the sea. At low tide the rock stood well out of the water, but when the tide was high the rock was covered and lay deep below the surface of the sea.

Now Lachlan MacLean remembered this rock and, just between dusk and nightfall, when there was no one about to see what he was up to, he made the Lady Elizabeth go down to the shore with him, and there he forced her to get into a boat. He rowed out to the rock and put her on it, and then he got into the boat and rowed away and left her there alone. The tide would come up as the night wore on, and the waves would cover her over, he thought, and he was very well satisfied.

Night fell, and in the darkness, Lady Elizabeth stood on the rock, afraid to move lest she lose footing and fall into the sea. Then the moon rose and the stars began to come out, showing themselves in the sky. By their light she saw that the tide had risen so far that the bit of the rock upon which she was standing was a very small island indeed. The waves, dashing themselves against the rock seemed to reach eagerly up toward her, as if they tried to grasp her and pull her down with them into the sea. It could not be long before they did, she thought, for already she could feel the spray of them rising against her face. There was naught she could do to help herself, so she crossed her arms on her breast and said her prayers, then waited patiently for death.

While she stood waiting, with her head lowered, her ears caught the sound of oars, and raising her head to peer through the uncertain light she saw the shape of a boat slipping along between the rock and the shore of the mainland. A crew of fishermen, benighted, were returning late to their homes.

The Lady Elizabeth cupped her hands to her mouth and called to them as loudly as she was able, and they heard her voice at last above the rushing noise of the waves. Quickly they came to her and lifted her off the rock and into their boat.

They were all men of Argyll and knew who she was the minute she set foot in their boat. And what was she doing alone on the rock at that hour of the night, they wanted to know. When they learned that Lachlan Mac-Lean had put her there, their anger knew no bounds. They would not hear of taking her back to Duart, but rowed straightway to the mainland, not contented until they had put her safe in her brother's hands.

The fishermen were so angry with MacLean of Duart that they would have had the earl call out the clan that very night to seek him out and give him the punishment he deserved. The earl, at first, when he heard their story, was inclined to agree with them, and perhaps would have done as they wished. In spite of her distress at what had happened, the Lady Elizabeth begged her brother to let it pass, since she was safe now, and at home. If there was to be a feud, she told him, it would be the people of Duart who would suffer, and they had given her kindness and friendship beyond measure in her days when she had been so unhappy on their isle. They would be bound to come to the aid of their chieftain if the earl marched against him, and likely enough, he would take to his heels and escape and leave his followers to bear the brunt of the fight.

At first the earl would not listen, but paced up and down the hall, shouting threats against MacLean. But the Lady Elizabeth followed after him, and little by little she won his ear. Although it was her pleading that partly persuaded him, it was a thought of his own that finally made him consent to wait for his revenge. Although the earl's anger was still black and seething, he was begin- ning to be curious to know how Lachlan MacLean was going to explain the disappearance of the Lady Elizabeth. He'd have to find some sort of explanation to give her brother, who was the head of the family into which Lachlan MacLean had married, and the chief of the Argyllshire clans as well.

"We'll bide a bit," the earl told the fisherman, "and see what MacLean's next move will be."

The fisherman could see the sense of that, after all. "Aye, let the rogue think his scheme has succeeded," they agreed.

So the earl decided to do nothing for the present, and got the fishermen's promise to tell nobody what they had seen and heard that night. The presence of Lady Elizabeth must be concealed from the world outside the castle, and the earl's family and his attendants in the castle were sworn to keep it secret, too.

Thus Lachlan Cattanach MacLean had no knowledge of what had happened. He took it for granted that the Lady Elizabeth had met the fate he had so wickedly contrived for her. Now he sent word to the Earl of Argyll that the Lady Elizabeth had fallen ill of a fever, and naught they could do could save her, so the poor lady had died.

The Earl of Argyll sent word back that he was greatly grieved to hear the news, and Lachlan MacLean must bring back the Lady Elizabeth's body at once, that she might be buried in the Argyll churchyard, beside the graves of her ancestors.

Lachlan MacLean was terribly dismayed at the earl of Argyll's request, because, of course, he had no body to take to the earl. But his wicked mind soon found a way to get around that obstacle. He got hold of a coffin and then he made a figure of sticks and straw. He wrapped it all about from head to foot with winding sheets, and laid it in the coffin, and nailed the lid down tight.

He gave out word to his people at Duart that his dear wife, the Lady Elizabeth, was dead of a fever that had carried her off quickly, and, as was only right, he'd be carrying her back to Argyll, to her brother.

The Duart folk were greatly saddened, for they had held their mistress dear, but they were startled, besides, to hear that she was dead. It seemed a very sudden thing. But, they said, it was often so with fevers. They often ended in just that way. When the fever struck badly, death could come soon. They remembered that they had not seen the Lady Elizabeth about for several days, and some of them had wondered, for she was often in the village looking after the people there.

Lachlan MacLean was pleased to find that no one asked inconvenient questions, but believed exactly what he said. He chose a large company of followers to go with him, to carry the coffin of the Lady Elizabeth back to Argyll in great state.

When the company of mourners came to the castle of the Earl of Argyll it made a brave display. Lachlan MacLean headed the funeral procession, all clad in black and making a great show of grief. Behind him walked a long line of his men bearing with them the coffin of the Lady Elizabeth.

The Earl of Argyll met them at the door and bade them set the coffin down in the hall. He had servants take away the men who had come from Duart, that they might be cared for after their journey, but MacLean he kept with himself. Very gravely, the earl listened to Lachlan MacLean as he spoke of his great sorrow, but the earl said nothing until the man had finished.

Then the earl said, "We are just about to sit down to dinner. Will you join us, Lachlan MacLean?"

The earl threw open the great doors of the dining hall and moved aside for him to enter. Lachlan MacLean stepped into the room — and there he stopped, as if turned to stone!

There before his horrified eyes at the head of the table, facing him, sat the Lady Elizabeth. Standing behind her and on either side of her stood all the chieftains of the Earl of Argyll's clan.

Nobody spoke to him. Nobody made a move to touch him. The earl had given orders that no sword of Argyll should be soiled by the blood of a creature so low as MacLean. But their cold, accusing eyes struck such terror to his heart that he put up his hands to his own, to shut out the sight.

Then Lachlan Cattanach MacLean, turning, fled from the Earl of Argyll's castle. Fled, too, from his own castle of Duart, for his people would have no more of him after they learned what he had done. In the end, he fled from the Highlands and the islands to return no more.

King James V
1531 A.D.

I n the turbulent times of James V of Scotland, beggars were the bane of the country. Strapping big fellows they were, with little taste for toil, so they went foraging about, living off the land. What they couldn't get by begging they'd help themselves to, without a "By your leave" before or a "Thank you" after. They were so clever at pilfering they could take the eggs from under a sitting hen and never disturb a feather, or steal a pair of shirts from a wash-line while the good wife had her back turned, pegging up the shifts. By the time eggs or shirts were missed the thief had taken to his heels and was over the hills and a mile or more away.

At last the beggars grew so bold and so troublesome that people clamored for help against them, so a law was made to keep them down. According to the law, if a beggar was able to work but unwilling, the sheriff would take him and carry him off to jail.

Not that there were no more beggars at all. The king had the right to license any man to follow the trade of begging if his Majesty pleased to do so. But a license was not easy to come by, for getting it depended upon the character of the man who asked for it. Licensing got rid of the worst of the old lot of beggars, and the ones who remained were, for the most part, honest and well-behaved. Folk even found them useful, for they picked up news as they went along, spreading it among the people so that they could know what was going on in the world at the time.

As a mark of their trade, and to show that they were licensed and couldn't be bothered by the sheriff and his men, these beggars wore a long blue cloak with a hood. They traveled from one end of Scotland to the other, and wherever they went people called them the gaberlunzie men.

One fine morn of early May a gaberlunzie man came striding along a country lane that led to a market town. Slung over his shoulder was a big leather pouch, very well filled by the looks of it, and he carried a sturdy staff in one hand. The day was fair and the breeze was cool and the skirts of his blue cloak swirled about him as, sometimes singing and sometimes whistling a merry tune, he stepped briskly along. He came to a place in the road where there was a bit of a hill of the sort that's soon up and soon down—the kind country folk call a thank-ye-ma'am. The gaberlunzie man swung up the hill at an easy gait and when he got to the top of it he looked down the other side. About halfway down the hill he saw a wee farm cart o'erturned in the ditch by the side of the road. So down he went and stopped to have a look at the cart.

"Och, now, and here's a pretty pickle!" exclaimed the gaberlunzie man.

And so it was. One of the shafts of the cart was broken, and the traces, too. There once must have been a beastie to draw the cart, but it was not now in sight. In the ditch under the cart was a sorry mess of broken eggs and honeycomb, and onions and such things that the cart must have been carrying to the market town. And on the bank of the ditch the farmer sat, with his head in his hands. There was no doubt about it. He was the owner of the cart. The poor fellow sat there mumbling and grumbling to himself.

The gaberlunzie man, having had a look at the cart, turned his attention to the man in the ditch.

"Och, my mannie, ye've had a bad toss," said the gaberlunzie man. "What mischance befell ye?"

"Mischance!" said the farmer, raising his head and glowering at the beggar. " 'Twas no mischance at all. The slemmers! The rogues! 'Twas what they intended to do."

"Och, aye. But who was it?" asked the gaberlunzie man.

"Who would it be, then, but the King's gentlemen," demanded the farmer. "Going along as if they owned all the road. They came riding two by two on their fine big horses, and not giving way to anybody, being so proud and great."

The farmer had given up half the road to them, for them to go by on, but they would have all of it, no less. So when they came up to him they crowded his cart off the road and never stopped when it turned over, but laughed at his plight and went galloping on their way.

"See for yourself," the farmer told the gaberlunzie man. "Here am I, a good five miles from my own croft, with my cart broke, my market wares as good as gone, and my wee horse off and away, and who knows where he's gone. 'Tis a black day, and all to be laid to the King's gentlemen."

"The King's gentlemen," said the gaberlunzie man. "Well, well! Was it indeed, now?"

"Och, aye. They said so, as they went by, telling me

to make way for them, they being the gentlemen of the king. But what can a body do?"

"Och, then, since you're asking, I'll tell you," answered the gaberlunzie man. "A body could maybe right the cart and get it back home to be mended. As for the wee horse, you need not fash yourself about him, for in the way of his kind, as soon as he's wanting his supper, he'll find his own way home. Come away, man! Dinna sit there greeting. I'll gi'e you a hand to the job, and we'll see what can be done."

The farmer took heart at the offer and clambered out of the ditch. The two of them set to work and before long they had the cart, right side up and on its two wheels, back on the road again.

The cart was sturdy and strong so little harm had been done to it aside from a scratch or two on the sides and the broken shaft. The broken traces were nothing to bother about and would be easily patched.

Once the cart was back on the road, the gaberlunzie man tossed his staff and his wallet into it and stepped between the shafts, taking the broken one in one hand and the good one in the other. Laughing, he said to the farmer, "I've been many a thing in my day, and now I see I'm to be a horsie. You push and I'll pull, and sooner or later we'll get the wee cart to where we're wanting it to go."

So off and away they went, with the blue-coated beggar before the cart and the farmer behind. By dint of much pushing and pulling, and maybe a bit of groaning and grunting, too, the pair of them got the farm cart up the hill and down on the other side, and back along the road over which they'd come that morn.

The farmer's wife came running out of the house when she heard them coming up the lane to the croft. She had been worried almost out of her wits ever since the wee horse had come trotting home with its harness broken and neither cart nor goodman with him.

She was very much put out with the King's gentlemen when her husband told her of the mishap, but she was so relieved to have him safe and sound and at home again that she made little of it.

"It could well have been worse," she said. After all, the cart had not been so badly dinged about that it couldn't be mended. As for the money its load would have fetched at market, they must just get along without it. And by the Lord's mercy the wee horse was safe and at home, forbye. Things weren't going so bad that they'd not have another load for the market, with the cart mended and all, by the next market day.

It did the heart of the gaberlunzie man a sight of good to see them taking their troubles so bravely. But as there was naught more he could do for them, he shouldered his pouch and took up his staff to start again on his way. But at his leaving the farmer and his wife raised a great outcry, and held him back.

Indeed, he'd not be leaving them, they told him, and him without so much as having a bite or sup! He'd turned back from his road and come a good ten miles out of his way, just to give them a hand with the cart. He could see himself, by the sun, that it was time for dinner. He'd not be going away until he had shared their meal.

The gaberlunzie man had taken a fancy to the friendly pair, so he said it would suit him fine to stay. He laid aside his wallet and his staff and sat himself down to tell them the news while the goodwife busied herself with the meal.

Kail brose it was, with barley bannocks, and all good country fare. 'Twas all they had to offer, the goodwife told him, but such as it was, he was welcome to it.

The gaberlunzie man snapped his fingers. "I've a wee bit of dinner in my pouch," said he. "I was forgetting all about it." He brought his wallet to the table and began to empty it out. " 'Tis only fair to share and share alike," said he. And first he took out a fine plump hen roasted crisply and brownly, and then a wheaten loaf was set beside it. "And now," he said, "a wee drop of wine will not come amiss to wet our throats and make us cheery." And he brought out a stone bottle from the bottom of his pouch, and put it with the things upon the table.

The eyes of the farmer and his wife flew open wide at the sight of food of the sort they seldom saw save on a feast day or a holy day.

"How did you come by that?" asked the farmer, his mouth agape with surprise. His wife looked sorely troubled. "Is it the way of the old begging-craft that you've been going?" she asked timidly. "Lifting things from the kitchens of the gentry?"

"Och, nay! 'Twas honestly got! You need not fash yourself about that. I asked for it openly and it was freely given to me. The folk that gave it could easily spare it."

"Did you e'er hear the like?" the goodwife asked. "He did but ask for it, and it was put into his hands!"

"Och, aye," agreed the farmer. "And if I were not

content to be as I am, a farmer, I'd be a gaberlunzie man myself."

" 'Tis not a trade you'd be liking at all," the goodwife told him firmly. "You're better off as a farmer. Come eat your dinner."

So they all fell to, and a very good meal they made of it, picking the fowl to the bones and leaving only the empty dishes and a few crumbs on the table when they were done with it.

" 'Twas a dinner the king himself would have fancied," said the farmer with a sigh of satisfaction.

" 'Twas indeed," agreed the gaberlunzie man. "And I'll give you a bit of news. The king himself had the same for his own dinner as we've been having this day."

"Then the king fares well," the farmer said. "Och, but how would you be knowing what the king had for his dinner?"

"A wandering body like me finds out many things of the like, and what's not handed out to him at the cottage door will be learned at the tavern, like as not," said the gaberlunzie man.

"A-weel," the goodwife said. "It suits me fine to hear the king fares well, for he is a very good king."

"Maybe so," said the gaberlunzie man.

"No maybe about it at all," the farmer told him earnestly. "And I'm thinking he'd not be pleased at all to hear how his fine gentlemen go about riding poor honest men off the road."

"That he'd not!" agreed the gaberlunzie man.

"A body ought to let him know, then," the farmer's wife cried out with indignation. "And were I man,

I'd go and tell the king about it myself!"

"I'd gladly go," the farmer said. "But the king is in his castle at Perth, a good two days away, and with my wee cart broke how could I?"

"Well, then," said the gaberlunzie man. "Here's a bit more news I happened to come by today. The king is not in his castle at all. He'll be biding this day in that same town that you and me were traveling to this morn."

"The king in our market town!" exclaimed the farmer. "Och, nay, you cannot mean it."

"Mean it I do indeed," the gaberlunzie man told him. "His fine gentlemen that shoved your cart off the road were riding to meet him there. A body would need no cart to get there. 'Tis not so far that his two legs could not carry him there. You'll ne'er have a better chance to tell your trouble to the king."

The farmer sat silently turning over in his mind what the gaberlunzie man had said. And whether because of the urging of his wife and the beggar, or whether it was the wine he had taken, to which he was not accustomed, the farmer grew bold. Jumping up from the table he cried loudly, "And I'm the body will do it! I'll go to the town this very day to tell the king!"

"Well said!" the gaberlunzie man exclaimed, clapping the farmer on the back. "And I'm the body will go along with you to make sure that justice is done."

So the farmer got into his Sunday clothes, and the gaberlunzie man shouldered his pack and took his staff in his hand, and off the two of them started down the road to the market town to see the king.

The farmer was brave and bold when they began their journey, and he had much to say about what he'd tell his

Majesty. But as they came to the town, his feet began
to drag a bit.

"I'm thinking maybe I'll not be bothering his Majesty
after all," said he. "Happen another day would suit him
better."

The gaberlunzie man would have none of that. "Nay,
man!" he protested. "Today's the day! Och, another day
the king will not be in the town at all." And he took a
firm grip on the farmer's arm and turned him away
from the road and into the high street of the market
town. Whether he wanted to or not, the farmer had to
go along, for the gaberlunzie man held him tight.

The gaberlunzie man seemed to know where he wanted
to go, and without hesitating, walked straight down the
high street to the middle of the town. They came to a
fine big house that stood a little way back from the street,
and the gaberlunzie man went up to the house and into
it, as if he owned it himself, and the farmer had to go
along with him, because he could not get away.

They came into a fine big room, the like of which the
farmer had never seen before. It was filled with gentlemen
very like those who had been the cause of his trouble that
morn. A score, or maybe more of them, were lounging
or moving about in the room, all very busy at doing
nothing at all. The gaberlunzie man and the farmer no
more than got into the room when one of the gentlemen
jumped from his chair and called out sharply, "Gentlemen, the king has come!"

All the gentlemen who were seated leaped from their
chairs to join the others, all facing the door and bowing
as if their lives depended upon it.

"A rare queer thing this is!" the farmer thought to

himself. He had stolen a glance over his shoulder to have a look at the king, but there was nobody there. Still the fine folk kept on bowing and scraping although there was nobody else in the room but themselves and the farmer and the gaberlunzie man.

The farmer edged up close to the gaberlunzie man and nudged him gently with his elbow. He asked in a whisper, "Och, where is the king, then?"

The gaberlunzie man gave a little laugh and answered. " 'Tis this way, my friend. As I see it, one of the two of us must be the king, and if it's not you, then it must be myself."

Then the gaberlunzie man laid down his staff and his wallet, and slipped off the blue beggar's cloak and put it aside. He stood there smiling at the farmer, and there wasn't a finer gentleman in the room.

The farmer began to shake with fright, and he cried out, "Lord ha' mercy! I'd ne'er have thought it! The gaberlunzie man is the king!" And he fell upon his knees.

"Come, come, now," the king said kindly, as he helped the poor farmer to his feet again. "Have we not been good companions all this day? Am I not the same man who helped you with your cart? And shared your dinner, and walked beside you to the town? You did not fear me then. Why should you now?"

"But I thought you were a beggar, then," said the farmer. "Me and my goodwife would never have been so familiar with you and so easylike, had we known who you were. Your Majesty won't hold it against us," he begged. "We meant no harm by it at all."

And begging leave to go home, the farmer turned to go away, but the king laid his hand on his arm. "You must bide with me a bit longer," he said. "Did I not come with you to see that justice is done? Aye, and so I shall!"

Then the king turned to the gentlemen who stood near them, watching and listening to all that was said and done.

He said very gravely, "This poor countryman is a good friend of mine who has a complaint to lay before me against the King's gentlemen. On his way to market this morning he was crowded off the road, his cart o'erturned and broken, his wares spoilt and his horse frightened so that it ran away. And by whom? By a company of the King's gentlemen, no less!" And with a frown at some of his listeners who were disposed to laugh, he continued more severely. "Some of you are inclined to make a merry dance of such doings. Now all of you shall pay the piper as a warning not to be tempted to do so again." And at that, he caught up his beggar's pouch and opened it wide. "Guilty or not, pay up," he said. "Pay up, my fine fellows!"

Around the room he went with the leather pouch, and out came the gentlemen's purses, and willing or unwilling, into the pouch chinked the money the king insisted on having from each one. Those who wanted to hold back he made give double, and as for the rest, they took it with such good will, that each of them tried to outdo the others, making a game of it to see who would give the most.

When the king was satisfied with the harvest he had reaped, he hung the bag over the farmer's shoulder. "There!" said he. "Take that home to your goodwife and tell her it came from the gaberlunzie man."

So the king bade the farmer goodby, and sent him on

his way rejoicing. And why should he not rejoice? There was money enough in the leather wallet to keep his wife and himself in great comfort all the rest of their days. But even more than the money, the farmer valued the fact that the king had called him his friend.

Well, the king was a very good king, as the farmer and his goodwife had so stoutly said. And the kind that would put on the blue coat of a beggar to go about through his land, making sure that justice was being done.

King James had a scapegrace cousin, Francis Stewart, Earl of Bothwell, and a rascal he was if there ever was one. They say Auld Clootie put the mark of his hoof on him while he was yet in his cradle, and the older he got the plainer it was that he was the devil's own. He once hatched up a plan to carry off the king and hold him for ransom in a lonely castle on a high crag above the sea. The king, being a canny sort of person, was having an eye kept on his cousin Francis at the time, so he got wind of the plot before Francis could carry it through.

King James VI 1592 A.D.

The king was so put out to hear what his cousin had planned to do to him that he flew into a terrible rage. He banished Francis Stewart from Scotland and gave out orders that he was never to show his face at court again.

Francis dashed off to the Border, where for a while he found amusement galore. When the king's officers came after him he'd skip over the Border into England, and when the English got tired of him and sent their soldiers to take him up, over the Border into Scotland he'd go again, and being too sly and too spry for any of them to lay hands on him, he had the laugh on them all.

But after a while he got tired of louping back and forth. The comforts in the castles of his friends along the Border were sadly wanting compared to what he'd been accustomed to at the court of King James. He began to think that it would suit him fine if he could patch up the quarrel with the king.

He wrote the king a letter begging his pardon for what he had tried to do and said he hadn't really meant it, but just did it as a sort of joke on the king. If his cousin James would forgive him and let him come back, he promised never to do the like again.

The king did not trouble himself to answer the letter. Instead he sent word to the governor of the castle in which Francis was staying at the time, and told the governor to tell Francis, Earl of Bothwell to get out of Scotland at once, and the farther away he went, the better it would please the king.

The governor was so distressed by the message that he told Francis he'd have to leave the castle lest the king have it down about their ears. Finding the letter had proved useless, Francis didn't mind leaving very much. But he wasn't discouraged. He'd just try something else. If he could only get to the king and talk to him, maybe he'd be able to persuade him to let him come back again. So he packed up and went to Perth.

He got into the town of Perth without any trouble, but getting into the castle was a very different matter. The place fairly bristled with guards on every side. Even when the king rode out he was well protected, for he was always in the midst of his gentlemen, none of whom were particularly friendly to Francis Stewart.

He took care to keep well out of the king's sight, lurking under shadowy arches and in dim doorways, but as the company passed by, he looked them over and wondered if maybe one or two of the lairds could not be induced to smuggle him into the castle somehow, so that he could get at the king.

One by one, he sought them out and tried to win them

over, but most of the lairds had little use for Francis
Stewart. They were willing to wager that he was up to
no good and they'd no mind to get themselves mixed up
in any of his plans. Few of them would pay him any
heed at all, and those who were polite enough to listen
to him turned him down, some gruffly and some with a
laugh, but all so flatly that he knew there was no hope
for him with them.

But the devil looks after his own. His luck was in, for
in the end he found two gentlemen who were touched to
sympathize with him, and seemed to be willing to give
him some help.

One of them was the Earl of Burleigh, who was the
older, and should have had more sense than to lend himself to anything Francis might propose. But the other
one was the laird of Logie, who had come to the court
only a year or so before, and by the time he had come to
serve the king, Francis had already been away for several
years, hopping back and forth across the Border, so Logie
had never met him before and knew little about him.

Francis being blessed with the gift of gab, soon had
the pair of them feeling sorry for him and believing that
he had been badly treated by the king.

The way he told the story, he had meant no harm at
all by what he had done, meaning it only as a sort of
joke on the king. It was his mischance that the king
had taken it seriously, and chased him away without
giving him a chance to explain. After all, the king was
his own cousin, and was it wrong for him to want to be
forgiven and be friends again with his Majesty?

The two gentlemen gave him their sympathy, but
when Burleigh found out that what Francis wanted

was to be taken into the castle secretly, he held back. But the laird of Logie was all for doing what Francis asked, seeing nothing in it but a daring adventure which would give them a bit of fun. He rallied Burleigh for being afraid, and Francis added his pleas, and in the end, although not too willingly, he agreed to help Logie to smuggle Francis into the castle.

There was not a bonnier, blither, gayer lad in the castle than young Logie, and he had a host of friends. The king himself made much of him and he was a great favorite with the queen as well. The trouble with Logie was that his love for excitement made him more than a little foolhardy, and he often plunged into adventures that landed him into danger, because he never stopped to think before he acted. His friends shook their heads over his high spirits and his daring, and patiently pulled him out of the scrapes he got into, over and over again. They warned him, over and over again, that the time was bound to come when he'd get into some situation that all their efforts would not get him out of, but he just laughed at them and went on his merry heedless way.

Now the time had come at last, for the plan fell through. In some way or other, the king learned about it in advance. Francis was stopped and hurried out of the castle before he got fairly in. He got away but the laird of Logie and the Earl of Burleigh were caught while trying to help him, and carried before the king to account for their share in the plot.

The Earl of Burleigh showed his good sense by admitting at once that he had helped Francis Stewart, but he protested so earnestly that he meant no harm but was only trying to make peace between the king and his cousin,

that his Majesty believed him and let him go. But Logie
treated the matter in his usual lighthearted, highhanded
way, and to the king's questions he would neither say
"Aye" nor would he say "Nay." Although Logie was as
innocent as Burleigh of any intention to harm the king,
his manner made his Majesty believe that he and Francis
were equally guilty of something of the sort. The king
grew very angry and ordered that Logie be arrested and
held to be brought to trial.

Francis Stewart, with discretion, had hurried away
and taken himself out of the country entirely, and Burleigh, feeling himself unwelcome at court, retired to his
estates. The laird of Logie was left to bear the full weight
of the king's wrath. None of his friends were able to help
him and they were all of the opinion that when Logie
was tried he would be sentenced to death for plotting
with Francis Stewart against the king's life.

Logie's friends knew him too well to believe him guilty.
They were sure that he had considered it a mad and
daring adventure to bring Francis into the castle, and
his only desire was to bring the two cousins together to
settle their differences in peace. But the king would not
listen to anything they said in Logie's defense, so his
friends gave up his cause as lost.

But there was one person in the castle who believed
that Logie's punishment was beyond all bounds of justice.
This was Mistress Margaret, a young Danish gentle-
woman who was a lady-in-waiting to the queen. She and
Logie had fallen in love with each other, and as the
queen looked kindly upon the match, they were planning
to be married soon.

On the day that Logie was arrested, Mistress Margaret, while passing through the courtyard on an errand for the queen, was deeply distressed when she met a company of the castle guards bringing Logie with them, and he in chains.

The guards hurried him by so quickly that she had no chance for a word with him before they had taken him away.

When her errand was completed, Mistress Margaret went to her room to weep over her lover's plight. But her tears soon gave way to a firm determination. She made up her mind to save the laird of Logie even if she herself were to suffer because of her act. And after taking thought she came to the conclusion that she could do it according to a plan of her own.

At the time Mistress Margaret was serving as chief waiting maid to the queen. It was one of her duties to sleep at night in a small dressing room, or alcove, connected with the state bedroom in which their Majesties took their nightly rest, so that she might be at hand if the queen needed her services during the night.

There was a large casement window in the alcove which looked down upon the street along which she had often seen Logie come riding in happier days. Mistress Margaret sat by the window and looked into the street, now empty, and as she sat there she laid her plans.

During the day she made it her business to discover in which room of the castle the laird of Logie was being held. As her time permitted she prepared those things she would need to help her, and, having some money of her own laid away, she got it out and put it all in a small purse which she put where it would be at hand.

That night when she was sure that their Majesties

were asleep she slipped quietly out of the door of their
room and went through the castle to the place where Logie
was being kept under guard. To the captain of the guards
she said that the king had sent her to fetch the laird of
Logie to him at once. He wished to question the prisoner
further, she told the captain of the guards.

The captain saw no reason to think that the message
was false. Mistress Margaret was the queen's chief
waiting-maid and often carried messages from the King.
So the captain brought Logie out and bade him go with
Mistress Margaret, sending along two of his guards to
wait until the king was through with the prisoner so
they could bring him back again.

Side by side, the laird of Logie and Mistress Margaret
went along the corridors of the castle, and neither said
a word to the other, with one guard striding before them
and the other coming close behind.

When they got to the state bedroom Mistress Margaret
told the guards that they were to wait outside until the
king was through when she would bring the prisoner
out to them again. The guards then took up their places
in the hall, one on either side of the door, while Mistress
Margaret, taking Logie into the room, closed the door
behind them, and quietly locked it tight.

By this time Logie had discovered that their Majesties
were not expecting him at all, for he could see by the
night-lights that they were peacefully asleep in their
bed. He knew something was afoot, but Mistress Margaret, with finger on lip, cautioned him to silence, so he
asked no questions, but followed where she led him. She
took him quickly across the room, while the king and
the queen lay sleeping soundly and never stirred as they

passed by the bed. Into her alcove they went, and there the window stood wide open, with a rope of sheets made ready on the sill. She had a sword and a dirk for him, for she knew his arms had been taken away. She gave him these now, with a packet of food and the purse in which was all the money she had in the world. Then she let him down, by means of her makeshift rope, through the open window into the street below.

Once out of the castle Logie had no trouble in making his escape. Mistress Margaret saw him wave a last farewell before he disappeared into the night. She sighed sadly, knowing that it would be a long, long time before she saw him again. But she shed no tears, for she knew that he was safe. She went to bed and slept soundly, not minding in the least that there were no sheets nor covers to her bed.

Beside the door the guards stood until morning came, waiting for their prisoner to come out again. They might have stood there longer had their captain not grown uneasy at their long absence, and come to seek them. Not until then was it known that the laird of Logie was gone.

Everybody made a great joke of it, and laughed at the guards who had so willingly let their bird out of his cage. Logie being a great favorite, it was only natural that all his friends rejoiced at his escape.

But the king could not see the point of the jest at all. It soon came out that Mistress Margaret was responsible, and he might have done her some harm in his anger, had the queen not taken her and hidden her away where he could not find her. Of course the queen, being a woman, was all on the side of the lovers. When the king demanded that she give Margaret up so that she

could stand trial for what she had done, the queen refused. She stood by the girl and kept her safe. And she argued with the king about it until he nearly went daft.

"The poor young thing!" sighed the queen. "The poor pretty young thing!"

"Poor young thing indeed!" the king shouted angrily. "She must just come back, now, and stand her trial."

"That she'll not!" retorted the queen. "First you'll have to find her, and that you'll never do."

The king growled and threatened, but it did him no good. The queen paid no attention to anything he said. And she kept on telling him that women always did foolish things when they were in love.

"Look, now!" she said to the king. "If it had been yourself in Logie's place, would I not have done as much for you?"

"Well, maybe," the king admitted unwillingly. "But still—"

"No maybe about it," the queen said warmly. "I would indeed!"

Morning, noon and night she told him how brave Margaret was to do what she'd done; how much courage it must have taken; how clever she was to think it all out; how difficult the queen found it to get along without her chief maid-in-waiting, whom none of her other ladies-in-waiting could begin to replace.

The queen knew well that the king was given to flying into fits of temper, but unless the offense was very grave, he'd soon get over being angry. So the queen bided her time and went on talking.

Whether it was the king himself who decided to let bygones be bygones, or whether the queen finally talked him into it, nobody knows. But no more than six months had gone by before the king gave in and told her Majesty to fetch her Mistress Margaret back again. So Mistress Margaret came back to be chief lady-in-waiting to the queen, as before, and the king said nothing more about making her stand trial.

But it was a very long time before the king forgave the laird of Logie. In his first anger at his escape, the king had proclaimed him a rebel and banished him from Scotland, with a price set on his head. Nearly two years had gone by before the king's anger had cooled to the point where he could be persuaded to listen to a word in Logie's defense. But when that time finally came, the queen and Mistress Margaret so coaxed and pleaded at home, and Logie's host of friends so petitioned at court, that between them, the king began to feel that everyone was against him, and to wonder if he had been a bit too hasty in his judgment, after all.

There was naught he could do but give in, in the end. So he sent word to the laird of Logie that he was pardoned, and if he liked, he could come back home again. That suited Logie fine, for his heart had ached for his own country, so he set out at once on his journey home.

Logie's friends were happy to discover that although he was still lighthearted and gay he had been cured forever of wanting to dash into adventures just for fun.

Back he came, and having made his peace with the king, was graciously taken into their Majesties' favor again. And the next thing he did, with the blessing of the king and the queen, was to wed the young Danish maid-in-waiting who had let him down out of her window, and thereby saved his life.

he Border between England and Scotland was kept in order by wardens who settled at times upon a day and a place to send their representatives to consider any grievances either side might wish to bring up against the other. So that those attending either as witnesses or out of curiosity might be free from being caught up and put in gaol, should anyone on either side have anything against them, a day of truce was declared. This truce, by law, lasted for twenty-four hours from the time the meeting began until the same time the next day. During the hours of the truce nobody could be taken and held for any offense committed at any time either in Scotland or England, and the law had always been solemnly obeyed by both sides.

One of these meetings for keeping order in the Western Marches once was held in a town near the river Liddle. Lord Scroope was keeper of the Marches for the English and the governor of Carlisle castle. The Lord of Buccleugh, Sir Walter Scott, was Warden of the Scottish Marches and keeper of Lyddisdale. Lord Scroope sent his agent, Mr. Salkeld, to sit for him, and the laird of Buccleugh sent his cousin, Robert Scott, to act as his deputy.

With a fanfare of trumpets, the meeting was declared opened and the truce begun. Mr. Salkeld and Sir Robert Scott came out and met and greeted each other courteously and then the two gentlemen sat down to consider

peacefully the business of the day. It was all very pleasant and friendly-like, and as there were no complaints
worth speaking of at the time, the meeting was soon
over. Mr. Salkeld went his way and Robert Scott went
his own, and they finished so early that there was probably twenty hours or more of the truce to run.

There were always many wild Highlanders from Scotland and English Border ruffians who came along with
the deputies to make sure that justice was being done.
At any other time, most of them would have stayed away
as far as possible from anything that had to do with law
or order, knowing that there was too much against them
for them ever to be safe. But on this day they relied
upon the truce, which had never been broken, to keep
them safe from being arrested for anything they had
done.

Among the Scots who came that day there was one
Highlander, William Armstrong by name, commonly
known as Kinmont Wullie, and the Highlands never,
before or after, bred a man so wild. Kinmont Wullie was
a reiver and a cateran, and his forays on the English
side of the border were as successful as they were numerous. He kept himself rich and his English neighbors poor
by running off their cattle and carrying off anything
that wasn't nailed down fast. It almost drove the English
daft to see him flaunting himself at the meeting when
they had so much against him, and they not able to lay
a hand upon him because of the truce.

The river Liddle runs along between Scotland and
England, dividing these two countries from each other.
The meeting being over and nothing more of interest to
be seen, Kinmont Wullie mounted his horse and started

for home, riding along the Scottish side of the river.

At about the same hour of the day, a party of Englishmen, numbering a score or more, set out for their homes, riding along on the English side of the stream. They had not gone far before they caught sight of Kinmont Wullie. He was all by himself, going along the opposite bank. He had not bothered to gather any of his friends about him for protection because of his trust in the truce.

When the Englishmen saw him jogging along there alone, it was too much to be borne. The truce was forgotten and over the river they went and after Wullie, who by this time had seen them coming. Setting spurs to his horse, Wullie tore off across the country at top speed.

Well, Wullie rode, and the English rode, and for a while Wullie managed to keep ahead of the lot of them, but they chased him for two good miles or more and they caught up with him at last. Wullie might have been able to hold them off, had there been only three or four of them, but he was not fool enough to take on twenty. So they bound him and carried him back across the river and over the Border into England to Lord Scroope at the castle of Carlisle.

When they brought their prisoner to him, Wullie reminded Lord Scroope that the truce had still a good eighteen hours to run and would not be ended until noontide the following day. On that account, he told his lordship haughtily, it was unlawful for them to take him at all, and as they could not hold him, he'd thank them to take off the ropes they'd bound him with and let him go home.

Lord Scroope laughed heartily at him, and said, "Now

that we have you, I think you had better stay. And if you ever leave Carlisle be very sure to come and bid me farewell!"

Then his lordship gave orders that the prisoner was to be kept well guarded in the castle of Carlisle. So Wullie was led into the castle guardroom and chained and fettered, and there he stayed.

The laird of Buccleugh was ill-pleased at hearing about the seizing of Kinmont Wullie. He took the breaking of the truce as an insult not only to himself but to Scotland in the person of his Majesty the King. To add to the offense, Wullie's captors had taken him upon Scottish soil, and so had been trespassing at the time, having no right to trouble a Scottish subject on the ground belonging to his own land. But he did not wish to be the cause of any trouble between the Scottish King James, and his cousin Elizabeth, the Queen of England, so he decided that rather than carry the matter to his king, he would try to take care of it himself. He made an honest attempt to bring about Kinmont Wullie's release by peaceable means, in spite of the hurt done to his pride and the affront to the honor of Scotland. First he wrote to Mr. Salkeld and asked him to take up the matter of Wullie's capture with Lord Scroope. Mr. Salkeld replied airily that he was sorry, but as Lord Scroope was not at present at home, Mr. Salkeld would not be able to be of service to Lord Buccleugh. The laird of Buccleugh understood very well that this was just a polite way of putting him off. But he laird desired to keep things on a peaceable footing so he wrote next to Lord Scroope and told him courteously but firmly that since Kinmont Wullie had been taken by the English while on Scottish soil and the truce had also been broken, on these two counts it was illegal for him to be held any longer, so would Lord Scroope release him at once and send him safely home to his own country.

Lord Scroope wrote back that he had no instructions to do so from the Queen of England and could not do as the laird of Buccleugh demanded. In his own opinion, the crimes of Kinmont Wullie were so numerous that he was better off where he was.

Buccleugh was beginning to grow very angry with each new obstacle that was thrown in his way. But still wanting to behave reasonably, he wrote to the British ambassador, and it began to look as if he might have some success in his venture at last. The ambassador agreed with Buccleugh and wrote to Lord Scroope himself, telling him to let Wullie Armstrong go free and forget the matter, it being his lordship's fault in the first place for allowing him to be held after the truce had been broken.

Buccleugh's hopes were not longlasting, for Lord Scroope paid no attention to the English ambassador, and Kinmont Wullie remained a prisoner in the castle of Carlisle.

The laird threw his hopes of settling the matter properly to the winds. "Very well!" he said to himself grimly. "Since they're not of a mind to be reasonable, I'll show them I can settle the matter in another way. They'll learn a thing or two, before I'm through—and maybe three or four, or my name's not Buccleugh!"

The laird had friends galore on both sides of the border. It was no trouble at all for him to get in touch with

some likely fellows in the town of Carlisle who were
willing to help him out. Within the span of a very few
days he had gathered an amazing amount of information
about the English castle. He knew the part of the castle
in which Kinmont Wullie was being held. He knew the
height of the walls, the number of guards by day and by
night, when they were changed and where they were
placed. He had learned the position of all the gates and
the doors on all sides, what parts of the castle were
untenanted, and where the walls were weakest. The laird
of Buccleugh had a gift for getting the kind of news
he wanted. Very shortly he knew the whole of the castle
of Carlisle as well as he knew the back of his own hand.

Buccleugh was chief of a very big clan so he had
plenty of men to call upon when he needed help. He
called up two hundred of his own men, and Robert
Scott, the deputy, mustered two hundred more. Another
three hundred or more came out under Burleigh and the
Armstrongs, the latter being Wullie's kinsmen and taking the matter as an insult to themselves. All held themselves in readiness, at Buccleugh's pleasure, eager to
move when he gave the word.

On the day chosen for the rescue of Kinmont Wullie,
the word was given, and an hour after nightfall they
came riding in from all directions to meet on the banks
of the Esk, some ten miles from Carlisle. Here they
waited until about two hours after midnight, when it
was judged that town and castle would be sunk deep in
sleep. They then crossed over the Esk into England and
moved on to Carlisle, taking such precautions to move
quietly that even the hooves of their steeds were muf-

fled in sacks. They bore with them ladders, pickaxes, crowbars, levers, and handaxes according to the laird of Buccleugh's orders.

The night was in their favor, for it was dark and misty with a fine rain falling. So, unobserved and in good time, they drew up below the walls of the castle of Carlisle.

There Buccleugh lined up his forces and assigned the places they were to take. He sent a company of one hundred men to guard the road to the town to prevent help from coming to the castle from that direction. Sixty men he chose to go with him to force an entrance into the castle and carry off Kinmont Wullie when they had managed to get him. All the others were divided into bands and sent to the various gates so that nobody would be able to flee from the castle to alarm the countryside and bring aid.

The laird of Buccleugh laid it upon them all that nobody among them should take a life unless to save his own, and that no plunder should be taken in the raid. Their only purpose was to rescue Kinmont Wullie and with that achieved, they must be satisfied. Having laid upon them their duties, he told them that when Wullie had been set free and brought safely out of the castle and was in the hands of his rescuers, three blasts upon his trumpet would give the signal that their mission was finished, whereupon every man should make off as quickly as possible and make for home.

The horsemen moved off to their places and Buccleugh with his sixty chosen men went up to the castle wall. The ladders soon proved to be of no use, for they were too short to reach the top of the wall. Buccleugh, un-

daunted, abandoned the ladders, and took his men to the back of the castle, where he knew there was a small postern door, which, he had been told, was in a part of the castle seldom used, where the walls were in poor condition. It was not likely that this door would be well-guarded within. Very slowly, so as to be almost noiseless as they worked, they managed by means of the tools they had brought to pry and pick out enough stones to open a place big enough for a man to creep through. Two of them crept through the hole they had made and found inside by the door only one guard, and he in a drunken sleep. Before he could rouse himself to give the alarm, they had him gagged and firmly bound, and then they opened the door to let their companions walk in.

The night watch came running at the sound of so many tramping feet, but Buccleugh's men overpowered them, making them captives and carried them along with them to the room where Kinmont Wullie lay. They bore Wullie off just as he was, wearing his chains and fetters, and because they didn't know what else to do with them, they took the prisoners they had captured along with them, too. When they got Wullie out of the castle his irons were struck off, and a horse which had been brought for him was given to him. As soon as he had mounted, Buccleugh with a great flourish blew the three long blasts which proclaimed the success of the rescue of Kinmont Wullie, and off the rescuers raced, carrying with them their reluctant captives from the castle night watch.

As the raiders rode by Lord Scroope's quarters with Wullie in their midst, he remembered what Lord Scroope had said to him the day they brought him in as a prisoner.

"Hey, Lord Scroope, are ye waukin'?" shouted Wullie, as he passed by under his lordship's window. "Ye bade me be sure to bid ye farewell when I left Carlisle. An' sae I do! Farewell t'ye, Lord Scroope!"

By this time, the whole town, awakened by the voices, the trumpet, the pounding of the hooves of so many galloping horses, had given the alarm. Drums were beaten, bells were rung, and watchfires lit to warn the countryside. But they were too late for the laird of Buccleugh and his men. They had vanished into the night, with the rain and the mist to hide them, and long before the town of Carlisle or the castle really knew what had happened, they had all crossed back over the river Esk into Scotland again, and in good time came safely home.

As Buccleugh had ordered, not a life was taken in the raid, and not so much as a kerchief stolen and carried away. As for the captives, they were released and sent back to Carlisle in the morn, with a message to Lord Scroope, bidding him in the future to have a care to keep the law of the truce.

And Kinmont Wullie went on running off the cattle of his English neighbors across the Border in many a reiving raid, but they never caught up with him again.

ne fine night when King James went to bed he was King of Scotland—and of the Western Isles, when their chiefs would let him be —and he was nothing more. But in the middle of the night a messenger came riding at top speed from London and woke him up from a sound sleep. What the messenger had to tell him was that he was not only King of Scotland, but of England, Ireland, and Wales as well. The English Queen Elizabeth, God rest her soul, had died and left him her crown. It was all very sudden and it added quite a lot to the royal responsibilities, so King James decided to move his household to London so as to be in touch with his new duties there. So off and away to London they went, the king and the queen and all the royal family, the courtiers and the hangers-on, the gillies and the house servants, and Archie Armstrong, the king's fool that he kept to amuse him. They all went along with the king so that he wouldn't feel lonely in the strange place.

There were those who said that the reason the king went to England was because there was better hunting there than he'd ever find in Scotland, and maybe there was bit of truth in that. His Majesty had a great fondness for hunting, and often rode out for the pleasure of it when the weather was fine. His love of the chase was extended only to the hunting of the deer, for he could not bear the hunting of foxes or any other such game in which the English took such delight. When he got to a hunt and found out that a fox was the quarry, he'd turn his horse about and leave in a pet and go home.

But though his love for chasing the deer was so great, there was something he liked even better. The king loved dogs. His kennels behind the stables in London were enormous and there were said to be over a hundred dogs in them, of all sorts and breeds and sizes, both large and small. The kennelmen said that the king himself had no notion of how many there were, and as he was always adding to his collection, to say nothing of the litters of young ones that were born in the kennels, it was not easy to keep count.

The king's passion for dogs was soon well-known, and anybody who had a dog that was outstanding in appearance, character or performance learned to keep it well hidden when King James came to call, or the dog would most likely go along with the king when he went home. Many a man, to his sorrow, lost a favorite animal in just this way.

Among his dogs the king had one to which he was particularly attached. It was a beast of such great beauty that the king gave it the name of Jewel. The king never tired of pointing out its attractions, praising its fine head, its bonnie sleek coat, and its long silky ears. When he was at home he kept the dog by him, and even when at table fed it with choice bits from his own plate. No other dog in the king's possession was so spoilt and pampered as his beloved Jewel.

One day the king went off hunting and left Jewel in the queen's care, telling everybody that he'd be back in a fortnight's time. When he'd been away some ten days or so, the queen, to amuse herself, went into the garden to practice shooting at the butts. The dog Jewel followed the queen and her party out of the house, and was running about here and there. The queen took up her bow and aimed her arrow at the target, but her Majesty's marksmanship was very poor. Her arrow, instead of flying straight to the target, went sadly astray. At the moment, Jewel, running into its path was struck by the arrow, and falling over, soon expired.

The poor queen dropped her bow and burst into tears. "What shall I do?" she cried. "The king will have my life when he hears that I have killed his Jewel!"

The whole castle was turned upside down. Here was the king, expected home in a day or two, and everybody knew the temper his Majesty had, and of his way of flying into a rage and hitting out at anybody that was handy when anything went wrong. His fits of fury were as short as they were wild, and he was soon over them, but by that time a lot of damage usually had been done. There wasn't a body in the castle from the queen herself to the lowest scullery lad in the kitchen that didn't go about in fear and trembling at the thought of what the king was going to do when he found out that his Jewel was dead.

Then of a sudden, the same question rose in every mind. Who was going to take it upon himself to tell the king?

Nobody had a desire to get in the way of a temper as hot as the hobs of the devil's own place by bringing him the bad news. The courtiers flatly refused to do it, shuddering at the thought, and most of them suddenly remembered that they had pressing business elsewhere which

would take them away for a week or two, and left at
once. Her Majesty wept and said she'd never dare, and
the very idea of doing it made her so ill that she took
to her bed. Even Lord Cecil, for whom the king had a
great affection, when he was asked to do it, shook his
head and said, nay not he! He had too much of the king's
business to look after, so they'd have to ask somebody
else.

At last somebody thought of Archie, the king's fool.
Aye, they all agreed, Archie would be the best man in
the world to take on the job of telling his Majesty. Why
had they not remembered him before? So Archie was
sent for, and when they asked him if he'd be willing to
break the news about Jewel's death to the king, he did
not answer at once, but stood thinking it over, while they
all waited anxiously.

At last he made up his mind. "Och, aye," said Archie.
"I'll do it, if ye like."

When the king came home from his hunting there was
Archie, waiting alone for him at the castle gate. The
king knew at once that something had gone amiss
because of the long face Archie wore.

"What's wrong, Archie?" he asked, pulling up his
horse.

"Och, your Majesty," Archie said sadly. "I ha'e news,
and verra bad news for ye."

The king grew worried. "Out with it, man!" he said
impatiently. "What's the news, then?"

"Och, well, I dinna like to be tellin' ye," said Archie.
"But the dog Jewel is dead."

The king flew into a terrible rage. He shouted, he

stormed, he cursed till the air about him was blue. He
vowed that he'd have the life of whoever was responsible
for the death of his favorite hound.

Archie stood by and let him go on until he had to stop
to take breath. Then finding a place to slip a word or two
in, Archie told him, "Aye, your Majesty, 'twas what the
queen said. She said ye'd be havin' the life of the body
that killed your dog."

"And so I will!" shouted the king. "And so I will."

"Och, then ye'll have to be killin' her Majesty," Archie
said calmly. "Seein' that it was the Queen hersel' that
killed the dog."

"Eh? What!" exclaimed the king, glaring down from
his horse at Archie. "Did you say, *the queen?*"

"Aye, so I did," said Archie. "Och, your Majesty kens
fine that the queen could ne'er shoot straight, howe'er
she tried. She aimed for the target, but got the dog
instead. Her Majesty, poor leddy, was in a terrible
taking about it. She's been ailing ever since and in her
bed, and will not be comforted. She says ye'll ne'er forgive her. Happen she's right," said Archie, looking very
sad.

"Forgive her?" exclaimed the king. "Of course I'll forgive her!" His wrath was dispelled completely by his
concern for the queen. "Poor lass!" he told Archie. "I'd
rather have lost a dozen of my best hounds than have her
Majesty so distressed!"

He got down from his horse and walked along beside
Archie toward the house.

"Where is everybody, Archie?" he asked, when nobody
came out to welcome him home.

"The lot of them ran away," Archie replied. "They all feared ye'd fly into a rage and kill them, too, for bringing you bad news."

"The loons!" said the king. "I'm none so bad as that, Archie!" Then he was struck with a sudden thought. He stopped walking, and looked at Archie. "But, Archie," he asked curiously. "Were you not afraid yourself?"

"Afraid, your Majesty?" Archie asked in surprise. "Nay, not me."

"Why not?" asked the king.

"Well, it was this way in my mind," Archie told him. "Your Majesty might weel kill off all the court gentlemen, because you could find enough to replace them twice o'er the next morn. Nae doubt ye'd be findin' a new queen if so be it ye must. But I knew your Majesty would ne'er put an end to myself. Where would you be findin' anither Airchie Armstrong?"

The conceit of Archie's opinion of his own value tickled the king's humor, and he burst into a hearty laugh.

"I'll not be killing you today, Archie," he agreed.

And as they walked on toward the door, the king said, "Now we must set to work to make matters right with her Majesty."

He found a groom to take care of his horse and then he took Archie into the strongroom where all his treasures were kept. From his store he chose a fine jewel, worth a thousand pounds and more, which hung from a fine silver chain. He put it in Archie's hands.

"Go now, Archie," he said. "Take this to her Majesty, and give it to her with this message, word for word, just as I say it to you. Tell her "The king sends his best love

to the jewel of his heart, and bids her accept this jewel
as a legacy from Jewel."

Archie faithfully delivered the jewel and the message
just as the king had commanded. Then the queen, understanding that she had been forgiven, left off her weeping. Dressed in her finest attire, and wearing the jewel
which was her legacy from Jewel, the dog, she went
joyfully down to dine with the king.

ABOUT THE BOOK

Text type face is Century Expanded; display type face is also Century Expanded, with hand-lettered initials. The book was printed by offset. For this book of historical tales, Leo and Diane Dillon's drawings evoke a sense of the ageless. The three-color pencil and ink halftone jacket illustration and the black and white pencil halftone drawings inside are in art-nouveau style, whose intricate line work forms a complex design, reminiscent of the picture books of the late 1800's and early 1900's, like Howard Pyle's *Merry Adventures of Robin Hood* (1883). Hand-decorated initials as in medieval illuminated manuscripts, adorn the beginning of each tale.